VICTORIA COLLEGE
No.

D1177699

PHYSICAL SCIENCE AND HUMAN VALUES

PHYSICAL
SCIENCE
AND
HUMAN
VALUES

A Symposium with a Foreword

By E. P. WIGNER

Published by Princeton University

Press, Princeton, New Jersey

1947

VICTORIA COLLEGE
No.
LIBRARY

Copyright, 1947, by Princeton University Press
London: Geoffrey Cumberlege, Oxford University Press

Printed in the United States of America
By The Vail-Ballou Press, Inc., Binghamton, N.Y.

FOREWORD

UNTIL recently, scientists have been largely separated from participation in public life. Some scientists, like Franklin, have been great public servants, but in these cases their scientific activity has been in a compartment by itself. They did not serve the public *as scientists*; their inquiries into the nature of the physical world were entirely distinct from their efforts in the sphere of human society. This does not mean that scientists have not concerned themselves before the war with social and human problems; it means only that most of them did not like to talk publicly about matters outside the sphere of their scientific endeavors. They felt that there was no need for it, and many of them thought it inappropriate to make exact statements concerning problems for which they had specialized knowledge and then to speak publicly about questions on which they could claim no particular authority.

During the war there were at least two groups of human problems with which scientists as such had to concern themselves. In the course of trying to make the work of the wartime laboratories effective they were often led to rather general human problems as, for example, the cooperation between groups with different backgrounds, the reasons for the desire to serve the community, and others. More important, at least in some of the laboratories, they felt impelled to discuss the ways in which the results of their work would affect postwar society.

After the war it soon became apparent that the scientist *as a scientist* will have to face social responsibilities and human problems to an increasing degree. Most scientists feel these responsibilities deeply, and the broad public, which has been made keenly aware of the impact of science on society through its spectacular applications during the recent war, has been shown that the scientists intend to face their social responsibilities squarely.

The Nuclear Science Session of the Princeton Bicentennial Conference gave expression to this intention. The general plan of the Conference, as it was mapped out in collaboration with the Bicentennial Advisory Committee, encompassed the two subjects mentioned above. The first day was devoted to the relations of the various educational, scientific and governmental institutions, old and new, and to the ways in which these institutions can further the growth of science. The last day dealt, in a sense, with the reverse of the problem of the first day, that is, with the influences which the work of the scientist and the scientist himself exert and should exert on society. While the first day was concerned with society's influence on science, the last day's theme was science's influence on society. An intervening day of the Conference was devoted to scientific problems of a technical nature which are not recorded in this book.

The deliberations of the first and third days of the Conference were edited and coordinated by Dr. K. K. Darrow of the Bell Telephone Laboratories and are herewith presented to the public. Dr. Darrow has had great success in recapturing the often intense but always informal atmosphere of the whole Conference. He was ably assisted by the staff of Princeton University Press and, in particular, by the untiring help of Dr. D. R. Hamilton of Princeton University's Physics Department. I wish to thank all of them for the unselfish manner in which they devoted themselves to this work.

EUGENE P. WIGNER

Princeton University

CONTENTS

PHYSICAL SCIENCE AND HUMAN VALUES

SCHOLARSHIP IN THE SECONDARY SCHOOL

F. T. SPAULDING

THE future of any field of scholarship depends in principal measure on the work of specialists in that field. It depends also, however, on the educational program, whatever it may be, which underlies scholarly specialization. A conference on the future of nuclear science may quite appropriately begin, therefore, by considering the beginnings of specialized education. Those beginnings are provided in the United States by the secondary schools—largely by the public high schools. It may well be a matter of concern to everyone interested in the future of scholarship in this country to determine how far the American public high school can contribute, and in what respects it cannot contribute, to the education of scholars.

There is reason to believe that *the American high school is not now, nor is it likely to become, an effective instrument for specialized scholarly training.* Why this is so becomes apparent when one considers the typical secondary school in the United States—the pupils who attend it, its responsibilities to these pupils, its size, and the duties of the teachers who make up its faculty.

The typical American secondary school enrolls almost every boy and girl of high-school age in its community. The chances are even that an American boy or girl of today will stay in school at least to the tenth grade, and they are two out of five that he or she will get a high-school diploma. The universal nature of the present-day high-school enrollment is often difficult for people not intimately connected with the secondary schools to grasp. Few Americans more than

3

forty years old ever attended a high school which enrolled even a majority of all the young people in town. For most of us, the picture of high schools and high-school pupils which we carry in mind is that of the group of comparatively well-to-do and academically inclined youngsters whose photographs appeared in our own high-school yearbooks. To make the picture accurate as of today, we must include nearly all the young people who twenty-five or more years ago dropped out of school before they had even finished the elementary school—the boys and girls who came from families too poor to keep on sending them to school, or who were not good enough at school work to make it seem worth while for them to go on, or who preferred a paid job to continued studying. With few exceptions, all these young people have been added to the group who used to consider at least some high-school education as a matter of course.

In its educational responsibilities the public high school has thus become part of the common-school program of the nation. With almost all young people coming to it, it must serve them all to the best of its ability. It still owes the best education it can give to those who are qualified for scholarly work. But it owes the best education it can give, also, to the very much larger number of young people whose interests and abilities are essentially non-scholarly—who may become victims or beneficiaries of the results of scholarship, but who will find their own futures in the factories, the stores, the business offices, the service jobs, on the farms, and in the homes of the nation, and not in the classroom or the laboratory.

Moreover, for all these young people, scholarly and non-scholarly, the public high school has responsibilities which go beyond those of formal schooling. For better or worse, the public schools of the United States have become the principal guardians, outside the home, of practically all the interests of young people of school age. The health of these young people, their recreation, their participation in civic affairs, even their personal morals, are everywhere regarded as charges upon the schools. The high school must not merely, therefore, provide instruction for these young people in the conventional academic fields; it must at the same time furnish a wide range of non-academic activities for them, encourage and supervise their participation in these activities, and in general act more completely *in loco parentis* than any other social agency in history has ever been called upon to do.

The school which must serve all these young people, and serve them in so many different ways, is typically a small school. The average American high school, just before the war, enrolled 140 pupils in grades nine, ten, eleven and twelve. In a school of this size it is obviously out of the question to provide for segregation of pupils of differing interests and talents. In most classes in the small high school, pupils of all degrees and kinds of ability must work together under a plan of teaching which is necessarily aimed chiefly at the average. Even in city schools, where the size of the school permits the establishment of numerous specialized curricula, it is seldom possible to differentiate within curricula —to offer exceptionally talented college-preparatory pupils, for example, a program designed especially for them, as contrasted with the program for the college-preparatory group as a whole. The scope of the educational needs it must meet commits every high school to a wide and varied undertaking. The size of the schools forces the great majority of them to carry out that undertaking in terms only of the most inescapable deviations from the average among their pupils.

Both the size of the school and the nature of its task affect the work of its teachers, and hence their necessary qualifications. A high school of average size has a staff of only six teachers, who must be responsible for the school's total program. If it is to allow its teachers to specialize even in a single broad field of instruction—English, mathematics, science, the social studies, foreign languages, fine arts, and the like— with no more than one teacher assigned to each field, and if at the same time it is to take seriously its responsibility for vocational work, preparation for homemaking, and physical education as well as for the conventional academic subjects, a school must have a staff of at least twelve teachers. For the average school even this minimum of specialization is out of the question; a single teacher must offer instruction in mathematics as well as science, or in social studies in addition to English. Moreover, in the large school and the school of average size alike, the staff must somehow provide for the necessary educational and vocational guidance of their pupils, supervise programs of extracurricular activities, and serve as personal advisers and confidants to scores or hundreds of adolescent boys and girls. No matter how fully a teacher's own education has prepared him to be a scholar in a given field, he cannot be that alone in the present-day American high school. He must in most instances go far beyond the bounds of his scholarship in his daily classroom work, and he must in addition be social worker as well as teacher if he is to bear his full share of his school's responsibility.

This brief description of the American high school as it is today will perhaps make sufficiently clear the impossibility of expecting the high school to serve on any large scale as a promoter of specialized scholarship. Both the circumstances under which high schools must work and the scope of their responsibility prevent them from singling out one relatively small and unrepresentative group, the potential scholars, in order to give that group the distinctive and highly specialized training that would be appropriate if their advancement in scholarship alone were at stake.

Nor is this situation likely to change, at least in the foreseeable future. High schools are, it is true, growing larger.

The school attendance of boys and girls of high-school age, already nearing the theoretical upper limit, is coming closer and closer to that limit. Very small schools are being combined into larger schools, as improved transportation and new forms of school organization make it possible for a single school to serve a wider area. But unless and until the airplane becames as common and convenient a means of transportation as the automobile and the bus, all the increase that can be expected in the average size of the high school will still leave the typical school too small to provide specialized scholarly training for the minority of its pupils who might profit by such training. And even if such specialized training wcre to become practicable, it is doubtful that the educational policy which determines the programs of most American high schools would permit it to be set up on any wide scale.

The bearing of American educational policy on this whole matter deserves particular attention. The policy under which the average high school in this country operates is no doubt in part a policy of necessity. In part, however, it grows out of a definite conviction, widely held not merely by school people but by the American public. This conviction is that both democracy in education and effective education for democratic living demand the avoidance of segregation, or at least, all possible postponement in the segregation of special groups of students. Because of this conviction quite as much as on the ground of necessity, American high schools are tending increasingly away from rigid distinctions among special groups of pupils. For courses in English and science and history, for example, which were originally planned with college-preparatory pupils in mind, they are tending to substitute, even for the college-preparatory pupils, courses which offer as much of value as possible to all pupils. Instead of requiring pupils to make an early choice of special courses or specialized curricula, they are tending to put off the election of specialized work until all possible benefits have been gained from courses which pupils need in common and can take together. Thus by intention as well as by circumstance they are directing a principal share of their instruction to the whole group of young people who make up their enrollment, rather than to the specialized needs of the group of potential scholars.

In so doing the schools are unquestionably, and usually with clear recognition of that fact, sacrificing various advantages which might be gained from preparing their intellectually gifted pupils for specialized scholarship. But they are gaining other advantages no less important. By so contriving their programs that young people from every kind of background, with widely different interests and abilities, have a continuing chance to work together on common tasks and in a common environment, they are making a major contribution toward promoting in America an understanding and appreciation of all kinds of people for one another. Of the public high schools of this country more than of any other institution, it can be truly said that they are doing away with that kind of discrimination that defeats the purposes of democracy. They will be hesitant to introduce into their programs any sort of procedure which threatens this achievement.

If, then, as a result of policy as well as because of its circumstances the American high school cannot be expected to make itself an effective instrument for promoting specialized scholarship, one may fairly ask whether any help at all can be expected from the high school toward laying the groundwork for scholarship. The answer is that the high school can do certain things toward the advancement of scholarship which will be of great and essential value. In particular, *the high school can promote a widespread appreciation of the results of scholarship, without which the scholar himself can be only partially effective. It can, in addition, help to single out those young people who are likely to make good use of specialized scholarly training.* But the answer also is that the high school today is doing neither of these things as well as they need to be done and can be done.

If it is to promote a widespread appreciation of the results of scholarship, the high school must obviously address its teaching to its pupils as they are rather than as it might like them to be. In the great majority of instances these pupils are neither interested in scholarship for its own sake nor likely to achieve this interest just because they are told that it is important. They are interested, however, in two colloquial questions: "So what?" and "How come?" A subject presented to them in such a way as to answer these questions about matters of real concern to them may both awaken their enthusiasm and earn their genuine and lasting respect. And a subject so presented may at the same time allow the school to identify those pupils who have the interest and the ability which will lead them beyond the immediate answers to "So what?" and "How come?" into a rigorously logical study of how those answers have been derived.

This means that direct and more or less widespread applications of scholarly subject matter, rather than its logical development, must be the starting point for most high-school teaching. To use science as an illustration, the high-school courses in that field will need to concern themselves very largely with what youngsters can *do* with physics and chemistry and biology, instead of with what they must know to be thoroughly grounded in those subjects from the scholar's point of view. "So what?" is a genuine question on the part of the average boy and girl. As an answer to that question, the uses of science which affect his or her daily life, and especially those uses which can be taken advantage of in such matters as repairing a radio or looking after the family car or preparing a meal, will be far more to the point than any amount of practice with Wheatstone bridges, Bunsen burners, or the dissection of frogs.

Emphasis on the applications of a subject need not, however, prevent the development of an understanding of general principles. "How come?" is also a genuine question. The answer to it, in science, inevitably leads to the laws underlying scientific phenomena. The process of answering it may lead also, if that process is skillfully handled, into an appreciation of the laws underlying science itself. But the process by which understanding and appreciation will most surely be imparted will be an inductive process; and the facts on which induction will have to be based will be facts which appeal to the novice and non-specialist, regardless of their appeal to the scholar.

To lead young people of widely varying backgrounds and interests through this inductive process will inevitably take time. It will take so much time, in fact, that by the end of the high-school course in most of the academic subjects few pupils will have had opportunity to sort out their knowledge into the orderly sequences which genuine scholarship requires. Pupils will at best be only at the threshold of scholarly training; the actual beginnings of such training, for those who can undertake it with profit, will have to come later.

But there is abundant reason to believe that in this way of reaching the threshold of scholarly training, many potential scholars will have been saved who are now lost. For the present methods of presenting academic subjects to high-school pupils are in most instances the opposite of inductive methods. They are deductive methods, emphasizing logical classifications of subject matter worked out by scholars for scholars. However well suited they may be to specialized training for scholarship, they lend themselves only occasionally and by chance to the preliminary education of novices. And they almost certainly repel many novices who have the makings of potential scholars.

It is largely because of these formal and deductive methods of teaching that the high school is today doing less than it can fairly be expected to do toward laying the groundwork for scholarship. The school's continuing use of these methods grows principally out of two factors—the training of its teachers and the content of its textbooks.

The majority of present-day high-school teachers are themselves the products of specialized training for scholarship. Few of them, to be sure, have received enough of that training to deserve recognition as scholars in their own right. The average teacher whose principal subject is science, for example, has had little, if any, more work in science than is taken by the ordinary college undergraduate specializing in that field. But the teacher's background, like that of the usual undergraduate science major, has consisted principally of an introduction to the tools of scholarship—definitions, elementary "laws," practice with scientific instruments and scientific equipment, long hours of repeating in the laboratory the classic experiments of science—all to the end that he may have at his command the classified knowledge and skills which scientists who are truly scholars need to use in advancing their scholarship.

To his pre-scholarly background the high-school teacher has added, as a result of the requirements for teaching certificates in most of our states, certain courses in education. At best, these courses have awakened in him, even before he has begun to teach, a realization that his responsibility as a high-school teacher will be very different from that of imparting to a group of interested and academically able youngsters the principles and procedures of academic scholarship in which he himself has been trained. At worst, the courses in education have given him a few stereotyped rules of classroom procedure, together with a good deal of miscellaneous information about schools and teaching. In neither event has his work in education done much to alter or improve upon his subject-matter background. He finds himself, when he enters the classroom, needing to do one kind of job and equipped to do another. In most instances he simply uses the equipment that has been given to him. Having himself been trained at least part of the way toward scholarship, unless he is an unusually imaginative and resourceful person he undertakes to train his pupils in the same direction. But because the great majority of his pupils are less adept and willing than they need to be even to be receptive to the elementary training he has had, he lowers his standards, "waters down" his subject matter, and as a result is likely to produce a course that is a contribution neither to scholarly specialization nor to any other well-defined end.

Despite the shortcomings in his own background, the average high-school teacher of science or the other academic subjects might produce more substantial results from his teaching if he had suitable textbooks to help him. The average high-school textbook in an academic field, however, like the average high-school teacher, reflects that field chiefly as the scholar sees it. From time to time authors interested primarily in secondary education, many of them high-school teachers, have prepared books addressed to young people in general in an effort to direct high-school teaching not so much away from scholarship as toward an appreciation of its results. Such books have in most instances had only limited use because of the criticism heaped on them for not being scholarly. The result has been that the books which have exerted and still exert the strongest influence on the high-school program are those which confirm the high-school teacher in his pre-scholarly approach instead of helping him to change it.

Thus the problem of enabling the high school to make its fullest possible contribution to scholarship is as yet unsolved. Its solution will require teachers differently trained from those now being graduated from most of our colleges —teachers ready to use the everyday things that young people want to know as a means of helping these young people to learn, instead of teachers chiefly prepared to impress on their pupils a logically ordered set of scholarly facts. Its solution will also require new textbooks—books which put first the knowledge and skills of value to boys and girls who are not committed to becoming scholars, and which lead by progression rather than by force to the rigorous discipline of scholarship.

Probably neither the scholar nor the specialist in secondary education can at present envisage the whole solution to this problem. The kind of training in subject matter which will enable teachers to do their most effective work with the young people who now fill our secondary schools can be determined only through observation, invention, and experiment on the part of scholars and specialists in secondary education working together. The kind of textbooks from which present-day high-school pupils can learn best and learn most can likewise be produced only by a joining of forces.

The need for cooperative action on the problem is great. The results which may come from truly cooperative action, in the form not of specialized training for scholarship but of an educational program better designed to add to the influence of scholarship and to encourage the selection of potential scholars, lend strength to the hope that scholars as well as specialists in education may give continuing thoughtful attention to the teaching of their subjects in the secondary schools.

DISCUSSION

BOSSHART: I am much pleased that Spaulding presented his paper as he did because I think it is healthy for us all to know what that problem is. But I am not quite so pessimistic as I think he is in regard to scholarship. First of all, if scholarship is defined as advanced competency in a special field, then a high school never has and never will produce scholarship. All we can hope to do is to lay foundations for scholarship and perhaps we may be able to improve those foundations.

Our conception of foundations for scholarship as we have it in public schools is a broader one, of course, than work in just a special field. We have ideas about attitude, health, and the will to do. We have also a sense of responsibility for what we call the "personality element." We recognize that the problem of the acquisition of facts and skills is related to the things that the pupils want to do. We find that each one of these elements acts on the others, either favorably or unfavorably, and that all of these are basic factors in the acquisition of the foundation for scholarship.

About fifty years ago the high schools began to be faced with the care of a greater and greater percentage of our young people. Before long we were under severe criticism for lack of scholarship. But over a period of forty years we have worked and produced evidence that we have improved in the production of foundations for scholarship, at least to the extent that we have met more difficult college entrance requirements. We find colleges asking for graduates of public high schools; businessmen and industrialists seek graduates of our schools. That evidence is incontrovertible in spite of some criticism to the contrary. Much of this improvement has been accomplished through better teachers. Two other important factors have been a better system of guidance and segregation, which Dr. Spaulding mentioned.

I do not agree with him that the fact that the average high school has 140 or less pupils is a sound reason for saying that we cannot improve our foundations for scholarship. In the first place, I do not know just how Dr. Spaulding secured that average, but you will find that by far the major part of the students are in high schools of more than 140 pupils. In the State of New Jersey the average high school has 650 or 700 pupils, and we find that we can make desirable segregation. I would also like to raise the question whether it is a wise plan to adjust the procedures in larger schools to what we can do in schools of 140 or less. Once it was my good fortune to work on a commission on "The school in the small community," in which I found out some things about the problems of those small schools. There are some possible consolidations that will produce larger schools; in other cases, where that is not possible, there are ways by which small schools can make adjustments to the individual needs of students far beyond anything they have done up to date.

What worries me most is the proposal that we adjust ourselves to the average; it seems to me that if we start with an assumption of that kind we will come to grief. We want to produce all that we can, taking into consideration the individual abilities of the youngsters who happen to be placed in our charge.

I would like also to consider whether the broader duties of the teacher are obstacles to the promotion of scholarship. Do their social duties and extra-curricular duties and parental duties and guidance responsibilities prevent them from helping our young people to acquire better foundations for scholarship? May I suggest that the fact that the teachers work with these youngsters in informal groups is the very reason that they can lay better foundations for scholarship. If you will read the books on a liberal education by

Mark Van Doren and Theodore Greene, you will find sub-
stantiation for the statement that success in laying the
foundations for scholarship depends in large degree upon
interests, personality traits, health, and social adjustment.
All the surveys that have been made of failure of pupils in
high school show that anywhere from 60% to 75% of those
failures were due not to lack of ability but to wrong attitudes, bad health, poor social adjustment, and similar causes.
High-school teachers who work with pupils in home-rooms
and extra-curricular activities find real opportunities to
help young people become more interested and powerful
students.

Does the pedagogical training that teachers receive in
their teacher-training institutions work against promotion
of scholarship? I cannot agree that it does unless it takes too
much of their time. Good results are being obtained in high
schools where we have teachers—if we can get money
enough to hire them—who have a fairly advanced experience
in their special field and at the same time a reasonable
amount of pedagogical training. Many school administrators will agree with Spaulding that a little less pedagogy
and a little more subject matter would produce better results.

What are the schools planning in preparation for citizenship? The high school at the present time is trying to produce a better social education for our young people so that
our social education may keep pace with our technological
advances, and to help them to solve in a democratic way our
great domestic and international economic and social problems.

As suggested by Spaulding, the school needs to provide a
greater quantity of general education in both junior and
senior high school. In having more history and science,
preparation for family life, etc., which everybody ought to
know, there is a tendency to squeeze out some of the sub-

jects that the colleges insist upon as necessary for admission. Naturally the problem arises as to just what subjects should be eliminated. I would like to inquire whether any particular subjects constitute the royal road to scholarship? This is a question that sooner or later will have to be answered.

Another tendency is to combine pupils in heterogeneous groups in order that they may have the experience of working together with a real cross-section of our population to prepare for living in a democratic society. Whether all work should be done in heterogeneous groups is highly debatable. The claim that such grouping is democratic is also highly debatable. Is the fundamental principle of democracy difference or sameness? Before we get through with this problem we shall have to answer that question. In the international field we have to call attention to the differences among people and to point out that many of those differences enrich human life and must be respected. We have to think not only in the terms of sameness but also in terms of difference.

Many of us are convinced that if we put all pupils together they will tend to adjust to what I always think of as a deadly average, and then we shall not be able to produce young people who can solve our technological problems, our political problems, or our economic problems. In some way there must be provision made for differences so that these young people may develop their abilities to the full. It is well known that to put pupils heterogeneously into classrooms, unless the teacher is very skillful and provides segregation inside the classroom, which some might call undemocratic, almost always leads to the discouragement of the very able pupils and the very slow pupils. This in turn leads to a lack of emotional poise, causes emotional disturbances, and produces anti-social people. In the high school after 1900, when we began to take in this heterogeneous group, we found out that a certain amount of segregation is necessary in order to help a young person keep his emotional poise and keep him happy, and that a certain amount of heterogeneous organization is necessary in order that he may have desirable social experience. Cannot a way be found by which desirable differences may be promoted and social qualities encouraged? People are not opposed to the recognition of differences; they do so many things as parents in which they encourage the youngsters to develop talents that are different from those of other children. People desire opportunities for their children which cannot be provided by heterogeneous grouping. They desire also democratic social experience.

I find myself in complete sympathy with Spaulding's remarks concerning the inductive method. The troublesome lack of interest of many young people is caused by the deductive presentation of logically organized subject matter. The inductive method in the classroom provides rich social education and also allows for differences. Inductive classroom procedures permit students to think and act at their own ability levels. Inductive teaching helps youngsters to develop necessary personality traits along with knowledge and skills. That is a fundamental principle of progressive education. The reason that progressive education has failed and has been criticized in some places is the lack of ability of the teachers and more particularly the lack of understanding on the part of teachers that they are responsible for helping young people to emerge with the right kind of interests and ideals and with relevant knowledge and skills. Teachers who have learned how to help children acquire both interests and ideals and knowledge and skills produce scholars that go far beyond the expectations of most critics.

College and high-school teachers are being challenged as to whether they will depart from the traditional formal presentation of subject matter. The teacher-training institutions are not the greatest deterrents to the promotion of inductive teaching. Often fundamental community traditions scare school administrators completely away from experimenting in education. Sometimes school administrators look backward more than forward. Teacher-training institutions are continuously trying to introduce better methods, but when their graduates go out into the field, they find it very difficult to carry out their newly acquired ideals. Not the least of the obstacles to the improvement of teaching is found in college entrance requirements. I agree with Spaulding also that the solution to this problem of the education of our young people for efficiency as individuals and as members of society, and the solution of this problem in regard to the inductive presentation of subject matter will be found only in the work and cooperation of the faculties of our colleges and secondary schools and of the people as well. I am not pessimistic about it—I think that we are making headway now and if we keep working together will make great gains.

FORD: Being in the classroom, I may be able to lend a few useful ideas. Both speakers have pointed out the tendency toward diversification which has existed since the turn of the century if not even longer. In the Harvard report, *General Education in a Free Society*, it is pointed out that in the seventy years between 1870 and 1940, during which the population of the country tripled, the population of the secondary schools increased ninety-fold: that is, from approximately 80,000 in 1870 to 7,000,000 in 1940. We wonder sometimes whether people who are prone to criticize high schools realize the tremendous task we assume and which has been met with varying degrees of success. Both speakers brought out the fact that we have been confronted with the problem of the Jacksonian principle of giving education to everybody and the fact that any tendency which indicates segregation is looked upon as being undemocratic.

In the large city high school in which I teach, we have about 2,600 boys and they come from all sections of the community, a cross-section of the city of Boston. I have been teaching college preparatory physics for a good many years, and in recent years I have come to question the value of some of the work that we are trying to do. I have tried to analyze the problem, and I must confess that it is indeed complex. As a result of observation I believe that in our attempts to practice Jacksonian democracy we have let the pendulum swing a little too far. Since the turn of the century we have seen the institution of various special schools. For example, in our Boston schools we have a course for bakers. I don't say that we don't need better bakers, but I wonder sometimes whether in our attempt to take care of the approximately seven million who are in our high schools we haven't forgotten the bright boy who should be taken care of according to the Jeffersonian principles of education.

Many of our pupils in the Boston English High School are boys who have declared their intention of going to college. Unfortunately they are not all college material. The result is that the group is diluted to the disadvantage of the bright boy. I don't think that we can say that the high-school physics teacher will accept the indictment of failing to do his job properly. I do say that sometimes he can't do the job properly, and the reason is that the material we get is sometimes of such a diluted quality that we cannot give the type of course which the colleges would like to have in a preparatory course.

I think that perhaps the difficulty goes back to the sixth and seventh grades where boys of advanced talents have suffered the effects of that dilution, particularly in elementary subjects such as English and arithmetic. They are thrown in with a heterogeneous group and accordingly are not properly trained in arithmetic. They are in with another heterogeneous group consisting of children whose parents suffered under the delusion that they must go to college. And the bright children suffer again in fundamental training in English, so that by the time we get them in the third or fourth years we can't teach them physics because they don't know any English. They don't know the meaning of simple sentences. I sometimes think that I should teach them some English and algebra and arithmetic and forget about the physics.

Now I don't know just what the solution is. Certainly we have to keep in mind the Jacksonian idea. We live in a democracy and the administrators in the field of education are doing an enormous job of trying to give an education which will fit the broad average. As soon as you talk segregation you are called undemocratic; but if we don't segregate, what are we going to do for material for colleges and for scholars who are needed for the future welfare of the nation? I don't attempt to offer a solution. But I would like to leave with you one idea. It seems to me that to cope with this catering to mediocrity in both the early grades and in high school, we should do something to find out early who the boys and girls are that should go to college, and then give them adequate training in English and in elementary mathematics so that when they reach college they will be able to do creditable work. Much has been done in recent years in the matter of aptitude tests. I wonder sometimes whether they could not be used successfully to a greater extent in the sixth and seventh grades.

Of course, as soon as you do such things you have to guard against the stigma which would be attached to those who are not college material. I think that might be done by accentuating the dignity and importance of many workers who do not go to college. It might also be possible to counteract in some degree this sense of stigma by integrating the work outside of English and arithmetic of these apt pupils with the work of the others in the school in group activities, athletics, dramatics, and many other ways that will come to mind.

W. H. TAYLOR: Most of us here are more concerned with the work the high schools must do because of the very great number of students which they enroll; but I want to speak of the problems which private secondary schools must face, because it is not often that I have an opportunity such as this to get criticism of scientists on their subjects. I want to confirm or have criticized some of the things which we try to do at Lawrenceville, which is a boys' preparatory school with about six hundred students. Of course our problems must be in some ways very different from those which Ford has alluded to; and yet we are actually faced with the same problems modified in certain ways. We have to guard against the imputation of being undemocratic, and we try to avoid it by trying to draw as largely as we can from every section of the country and from every social stratum. In everything we do in science, we are still trying to give what I suppose would be mainly pre-professional education—to give a good training in the basic principles of the fundamental sciences as early as we can and as intensively as we can for those boys who are at the proper stage. We are free to do so because we don't have some of the problems that these other speakers have mentioned. We are able to segregate in a way which would be impossible in a large city high school. We can set up small sections for a few able boys, and we are doing so, and I propose to continue to do so as long as people who are in a position to criticize don't tell me that we had better change our ways. I think that with the increasing importance of science to every man in this age we have to attack this problem with all our energy. In the past two or three years at Lawrenceville, one of the changes which we have made consists in beginning in an earlier grade (namely the tenth) some training in solid principles instead of restricting ourselves to general description and discussion.

Thus we make it possible for a boy who is really interested, as let us say half of ours are, to get a good start in some one of the sciences. Now you may say, "Isn't that stealing from the colleges what they can do very much better?" I think not; for if the majority of the boys who enter college every September come from public high schools where by force of circumstances they must have had a somewhat more preliminary education in science, the colleges will have to use all their skill and facilities to give good courses in basic science to those many, and should be glad to have a small number who are already prepared for advanced work. I stand up here as a sort of minority reporter, hoping that anyone who thinks that we are in the wrong on this will let me know.

HOGG: I speak with some hesitation because I know nothing of the high-school systems; but I have had a good deal of experience in private school work, having taught in Exeter for the past fifteen or sixteen years. In Exeter we are conservative; we believe strongly in the deductive process and we believe strongly in differences. It seems to me that we can make more of differences in the high schools; for in Exeter we find that it is absolutely astonishing what a young capable boy can do if he is led along in the direction where he has ability and interest. If we are going to stifle that, we are certainly stifling the beginning of a good student. I can speak with some assurance only about the work in science. When I first began to teach in Exeter the thing that struck me particularly was that the average boy or even the average student in the high schools today is taught one year of physics or one year of chemistry or both, and maybe a year of general science. The first thing that I was concerned with was the question of how much a boy could really get out of one year's work. It seems to me that education is a pretty slow process; there has got to be time for seeping in; and if to start in September and to finish in June is to conclude the whole education in physics of the average high school boy, I think it is inadequate. That was a fundamental problem in Exeter, and I think it is a fundamental problem in our high schools if they are going to teach science.

We run up against this perennial question of correct teaching—you see it in all the discussions of science teaching — Shall we begin with physics or shall we begin with chemistry? Chemistry leans much more heavily on physics than physics leans on chemistry, and if a boy is to do chemistry having had no conception of heat or electricity or hydrostatics or vapor pressures, he is bound to leave out a whole lot of essential concepts of chemistry. On the other hand we attempt to teach some electro-chemistry to physics students who have had no chemistry of any kind. It certainly is true that if a boy is going to take chemistry he should have had some physics. But if he begins with physics he probably hasn't had enough mathematics, and this is another difficulty. There are opposing arguments, and we find that some schools begin with chemistry and some begin with physics. Another solution is to begin with neither but to begin with both of them. This is one of the things that we have done in Exeter; we have called it a Physical Science course, and we consider it a very interesting experiment. I strongly recommend it to Spaulding as worth trying in the high schools.

Our course takes the boys over the better part of two years, and they have time to let the material seep in. We begin with hydrostatics and heat. The mathematical difficulty is negligible, so that we can actually begin in tenth grade. Then we go into the elementary descriptive work of chemistry with hydrogen, oxygen, and water, carbon and the compounds of carbon, leading on to organic chemistry; and we deal with the problems of weight and volume, including Avogadro's hypothesis, and still there are no difficulties. Finally we finish up the year with an introduction to mechanics, so that we are teaching both physics and chemistry without any difficult mathematics. In the second year we take up electricity. By this time their mathematical training has gone far enough so that they can use mathematical concepts. After electricity we go into ionization and carry on with chemistry; finally we finish up with light and sound. The interesting thing is that this is taught to very young boys. We have, of course, boys taking the regular one-year course; and we give both groups standard tests. The difference between the two groups is astonishing. Boys in tenth grade doing chemistry will be far ahead of boys in twelfth grade doing chemistry. Their advantage has been manifest every year for eight years, and we have measured it by giving three or four college tests each year. The difference in chemistry is quite marked. In physics again, the physical science boys are ahead of the one-year-physics boys who are a year older; but the difference there is not quite so great. In the third year the boys having done physical science for two years may take biology if they wish to. That is, I think, where biology really belongs; it should come after the boys have had some physics and chemistry and not before they have had any science of any kind.

We have also a Physical Science 3 course where we teach some rotational dynamics, the structure of the atom, and the interpretation of simple spectra. We like to have the boys doing calculus at the same time if we can manage it. In chemistry we stress equilibria a good deal and we illustrate the mass-action law by buffers and solubility product. It is something that young boys can do; it is astonishing what they *will* do if they are given their head. I think that our program could easily fit into most high schools providing it weren't squeezed into one year—provided that the teaching of sciences could begin a little earlier and spread over a number of years. That is the experiment we have made in Exeter, and we now have sufficient data to convince ourselves that it is sound as far as our school is concerned. I think that it may be worthwhile to consider it as a possibility for some of the high-school systems.

SPAULDING: There have been so many good things said that I hardly know which ones to pick out for comment. Most of us here are used to thinking about schools in the metropolitan districts, particularly along the Atlantic seaboard. If we consider the problem as a whole we ought to bear in mind that our potential scholars, our potential scientists, are not limited to this region. Our educational problem is a *national* problem and needs to be looked at in that way. From the standpoint of that national problem, may I add some further figures to those which I gave you earlier about the size of the average high school?

The school which I described as having an average of one hundred and forty pupils is the median high school in this country. The school which the median pupil attends is twice as large, about three hundred pupils (before the war). But, to provide for the type of segregation that would probably be desirable if we were to emphasize specialization in scholarship as the basis of our training, we should have to have a school of at least twelve hundred pupils; and schools with twelve hundred pupils are very rare in this country. We are accordingly faced with the necessity, over and over again, of making our program operate for schools that are far from ideal with respect to their size.

The question is not whether we want the schools to make a contribution to scholarship or not; we most certainly do. The question is how that contribution can be most effective. In the past, through a scheme of segregation which operated through the fact that the secondary schools were highly selective institutions, we could make that contribution or try to make it in the direction of the groundwork of specialized training. At the present time a more effective contribution seems to be not in the direction of more specialization in the secondary schools but in the direction of providing a base upon which a later structure of specialized training may be given by the colleges.

It is of interest to observe that the emphasis that the colleges are now putting on the need for general education on a college level is a reflection of the lack of general education at the secondary school level. The secondary schools have perhaps gone too far in attempting to provide specialized study at their level, making it necessary for the colleges to go back and do what the secondary schools might properly have done. If the secondary schools, regarding their job as that of providing general education, could lay the groundwork for appreciation of the results of scholarship and for the selection of eventual scholars, then the colleges could devote themselves more advantageously to a beginning of training in specialized scholarship as such.

THE RELATION OF RESEARCH
IN UNIVERSITIES
TO GOVERNMENT AND COMMERCIAL
LABORATORIES

I. I. RABI

I SPEAK simply as a university physicist, pursuing my research, giving bad courses and bad grades, attempting to get along with modest experimental means. My opinions on this subject come from a five year war experience, and may be irrelevant to the problem.

Before we start a discussion of the relation of research in universities to governmental and commercial laboratories, it would be well to consider the aims of these institutions. The universities' aim is to educate and provide new knowledge, so that university research is, to a certain degree, a part of the educational process and is parasitic on teaching. In university research you have professors who teach students how to do research and, incidentally, gain new knowledge. A professor has to interest his students and motivate them in their search for knowledge. A university professor is not an ordinary individual because he does not follow an ordinary calling. So there will be certain characteristics about his research that are traditionally associated with teachers. His impracticality is taken as a matter of course. This, then, gives a certain background to the quality of university research.

The aim of commercial laboratories is the improvement of products and methods. Even when this distinction is taken in its broadest sense, the commercial laboratory is parasitic on commerce and industry; it must retain the characteristics of these worthy causes. Somehow or other it must make money by selling a product or a service.

28

Government laboratories exist to promote the national welfare and the national security. In a democratic country such as ours they ultimately have to satisfy the people that they do this job. As public servants the scientists in these laboratories have to justify to every penny the expenditure of public funds. The ancient American suspicion that public officials are essentially rascals who seek to drain the taxpayer's pocket serves to provide a sense of original sin in all their activities. They must be practical, sensible, and economical with the public's money—and ostentatiously so—in order that no representative or senator be left unsatisfied.

Under these circumstances the relationships between university laboratories and commercial laboratories and government laboratories are bound to be somewhat different and one-sided. There is a certain amount of rivalry between government and commercial laboratories; but in the last analysis government is a customer for commerce and that makes for close and harmonious relations. Vis-à-vis the universities, there are great difficulties. First there is the matter of patents. One of the most important products of a commercial laboratory is a strong patent position. The acquisition of such a position is in itself sufficient justification for the existence of a commercial laboratory. But this does not make for frankness. There must of necessity exist a strong form of commercial security. The fundamental interests of a commercial laboratory are circumscribed by the reasons for its existence. It exists to receive and retain information but not to transmit it; at least not to transmit the information while it is still fresh and spontaneous, except in case of the accidental circumstance of its having no conceivable practical importance for seventeen years. Strangely enough, government laboratories have the same patent consciousness. When this is coupled with military security we get what amounts to a system surrounded by a semi-permeable membrane. Knowledge can diffuse inward, it is true, but with some difficulty; and nothing comes out except by reason of the imperfections of the membrane.

I will not maintain that the picture which I have given is accurate at the moment. These are unsettled times and many people in these three varieties of laboratories have been together in great war projects. They still maintain some of the habit of talking to one another but my picture is certainly fairly accurate for the pre-war period, and there are some indications that the fundamental causes remain unaltered.

Should the universities become more like the commercial laboratories and the government laboratories? I think not. Our problems are getting to be so serious, so practical, and so regimented that we should not endanger the existence of the little oasis that is free and not under the direct necessity of continually justifying itself in the material sense. The war emergency has shown that a university scientist can easily be turned into a war worker when the emergency arises. The war has also shown that the kind of knowledge and point of view which is gained in the university can be turned into extraordinarily useful channels. It is perhaps unwise to tamper with the source of this fund of human material and knowledge.

Should the reverse process be considered? Should the university point of view be taken up by the government and commercial laboratories? Such a movement is indeed now underway. It may be a good thing, or it may turn out to be disruptive to the normal activities of these organizations. It is a matter of education of those who control commerce and industry and of the general public. If an appreciation of science as a vital activity of our culture, and not only as a passport to technology, becomes widespread, there will be no harm done. Otherwise each kind of laboratory must and will retain its essentials and its redeeming features. I want to make clear that we are all aware of the vital and fundamental importance which technology plays in the advancement of pure science. Think where we should be in nuclear physics or cosmic rays without the thermionic valve! What I have said is not a degradation of technology but an attempt to see the true relationships among these three types of laboratories.

In the universities we are in a particularly critical time in the matter of support. It is a fact in the subject of physics now, as in many other things, that enormous amounts of money are available for the support of research. *But if it were decided to control universities and university research, there could be no better way to do this than the way it is being done now.* Distributing large funds brings the distributors to the position in a short time of being able to apply certain pressures to the universities to change their method of working, to justify their activities, and conform their policies with other broad national and governmental activities. This would look not unreasonable but for the fact that it must impair those very special features, those very special contributions which universities make to our whole national outlook.

DISCUSSION

CONDON: I very much object to any derogatory use of the term that university research is parasitic on teaching. To be parasitic on something is certainly one of the characteristics of most research. Perhaps it is a good thing to get across the idea that for its own sake research really should be supported *indirectly.* I like the idea of what I will call "bootleg research" simply because it's one way of insuring freedom. If you frankly and openly get your support for research as such, then you are under an obligation to produce in a manner that conforms with the ideas of the persons that support you rather than your own ideas. This doesn't confront you if you are a researcher of the parasitic or bootleg type. For example, in the university, I think the greatest thing about the research is that it is parasitic on teaching, the fact that the universities to a large extent don't have to support it. One would not say that university administrations are opposed to research and that you have to put it over in a dark alley without their knowing anything about it. The point is that it is parasitic in the sense that there is not, generally speaking, any university administrative control over the subject matter. The same thing is true in the commercial and government laboratories where the aim is somehow or other to attain certain ends; the research as such is auxiliary to a different aim and hence the research men are less scrutinized as to exactly what they do.

Rabi spoke about the justification of expenditures which the government people have to make. I do not deprecate it, even though I happen to be one of those who will have to be on the spot to testify when those conditions return. I think that there has grown up in recent years, especially over the war period, altogether too much of a tendency to get large expenditures for things in the government which are not carefully scrutinized and which, although they put on a large ostentation of being practical, sensible, and economical, are not so much so as they should be. That of course is especially true in military matters.

Numbers in the government are so big that we are likely to forget the decimal point. It might be worthwhile to recall, for example, that in this year's federal budget the expenditures directly attributable to military activity are ten times the total aggregate expenditures of all the other executive departments put together, namely the executive departments of a strictly civilian character, Post Office, Interior, Commerce, Agriculture, and so forth. In the aggregate these are about 1.8 billion dollars. In the aggregate, military expenditures this year are about 18 billion dollars. Military expenditures in one year of peace are three times what was considered a rather big budget ten years ago for the entire federal government. If this country is so rich that it can afford these things, then surely we can afford some things of the character of peaceful efforts. Yet we debated a long time and have not yet appropriated anything but a few million dollars for Unesco. This, in the same country that could spend something like fifty per cent more for the Bikini atomic bomb test than it cost to build Boulder Dam! Anyway, for our little show at Bikini—it's all over now and all we are going to get out of it is gotten—we spent more than the maintenance of Princeton University costs on a steady permanent endowment basis.

About patents, I should like to ask Rabi what he meant by saying that the government laboratories have the same patent consciousness as the commercial laboratories. I suppose he had in mind military laboratories because they have so dominated the scene in recent years, but I don't think that the patent consciousness there is the same as in the commercial laboratories. With the government laboratories it is more of a question of getting results that can be dedicated to the public interest than of getting results that can be retained privately by the government. That opens up a very large field of controversial thought and could easily serve to open up another argument: the whole question of how patents arising from federally financed research should be handled. One of the remarkable things about the existing situation is the complete lack of uniformity or definiteness about federal policy in this respect, in that each executive department seems to do as it pleases and, more than that, does it in a way that very much smacks of horse-trading. The military departments will attempt to enter into contracts with people which are very one-sided in favor of the government; these people refuse to accept such conditions and force the military departments to accept contracts that are perhaps unfair to the public interest in other ways. What is fair and what is unfair is of course a matter of opinion, but I think it fair to say that the government interest requires that all patents resulting from research financed completely by the federal government should become its property for free dedication to all users. I think the simplest way to do that would be to avoid the patent technique altogether and instead to give free publication in definite enough terms so that the subject matter resulting would not come within the patent franchise. I feel that if we were to look into the whole question of what went on during the war we should find that many inequitable things were done in the way of giving to private corporations patent privileges growing out of military research, in addition to giving them complete monetary compensation for all expense involved.

The question was asked: should the university point of view be taken up by the commercial laboratories and the government laboratories? I think that the answer to that is "yes, as much as possible." That spirit of free research and complete freedom of an individual to work by his own method, which is a characteristic of university work, should be followed in all research laboratories and I think it will be possible to do better in this regard as time goes on.

When Rabi spoke about the debt that we all owe to technology and science, I was reminded that the best expression of that idea that I ever heard is that of Herbert Spencer. Spencer said that "the sciences are arts to one another." Each science does not only make advances in its own field, but provides the technical means for which advances are made in other fields.

MEES: I couldn't help feeling shocked that an eminent scientist should say that science is parasitic on anything. Scientists in a commercial laboratory are not parasitic at all. I won't argue about the universities—it doesn't become the commercial scientists to argue about the position of the university scientist—but commercial science is a function of commerce. It is a part of the operation of industry. The industry is dependent on it, and the scientist is supported by the industry which he produces. That's not being parasitic. Research in industry is no more parasitic than my heart is parasitic on my head, or vice versa. They operate as parts of the same organism. I think the same is true of the universities; my own belief is that the first function of the university is the advancement of knowledge and the next function is the distribution of that knowledge and the production of new people to advance knowledge. I don't think that I should acknowledge, if I were a university professor, that my scientific research was parasitic on anything. I think that I should put the advancement of knowledge as the first function of the university.

Now, if we take the view that production of knowledge is a major function of the university or of the industry or of the government, what is going to be the relation of these three to each other?

In the first place, we must remember how important this advancement of science is. The whole frame of the western world, the whole development of the United States, the improvement in the scale of living of all, comes from science and from nothing else. It does not come from the activities of lawyers or the activities of commercial men, or even from the activity of the university professor. It comes from the production of knowledge and its application to our needs. And as that knowledge is produced and is developed year after year and decade after decade, it shows itself to the common people, who know not whence it comes, as an advancement in the scale of living. They demand this advancement, and rightly; and they will get it only if advancement of knowledge continues.

The laboratories, the organisms that produce this knowledge, are necessarily of two kinds. There are those which are "convergent" and operate in one field of knowledge, converging on the problems of that field the skills of various trades; and there are those which are "divergent," dealing with many branches of knowledge which come to them from various sources. For instance, the greater part of university work is divergent production of knowledge. Men do whatever comes before their eyes. They think of things and study them, originally stimulated perhaps by curiosity or possibly by deep thought, but in any case carrying out their own wishes. That is the fundamental and necessary freedom of science which finds its stronghold in the university. But the same sort of divergent research occurs in many industrial laboratories. All industrial laboratories have to do much research upon the problems that arise in the course of their work. Also it occurs on a very great scale in the government laboratories. But there occurs in all these types the convergent laboratory, the specialized research institute, perhaps established by a foundation, of which there are such wonderful examples as the Geophysical Laboratory, Mt. Wilson Observatory, and many others. It may be a professor in a university who establishes a convergent laboratory, studying one group of problems, drawing around him students attracted to him by the problems he is interested in, teaching them to work on these problems and bringing in new students year after year and thus developing a school of study which is a research institute. Or you may have an industrial laboratory or research institute which will study the problems of some specific field; the problems for instance that arise in connection with oscillating circuits, in connection with the problems of producing electric light by various methods, or in the case of the laboratory which I have the honor to head, the problems that arise in the science of photography.

We are going to need both convergent and divergent laboratories in the future. How much can they cooperate?

First of all, the convergent groups cooperate to a very large extent; the industrial laboratories cooperate with each other to an amount which would astonish those who are not accustomed to work in industrial laboratories. They have their specialized skills and interchange them. For instance, if I have a problem in electricity which is beyond our ordinary knowledge and I feel that Suits of General Electric knows something about it, I never hesitate a minute to call him up or go down to him and ask him about my problem; and I find that many of my friends will act conversely, when they have photographic problems they come to me with them and we try to help them. That sort of cooperation goes on between the industrial laboratories, it will also go on between the industrial laboratories and the universities, it will go on between the universities and the government laboratories, and between the industrial laboratories and the government laboratories. The process depends primarily on the individuals, upon their good will, upon their interest in helping each other and in increasing the growth of science.

There has arisen a growing relation between industrial laboratories and the university, or industrial concerns and university laboratories and university professors. I refer to the fact that there is a good deal of industrial consulting work going on in the universities. This gives me some concern, not because I think that these things should not be done, but merely because I'm afraid of some conceivable consequences. In particular, the university laboratories might be diverted from the advancement of science to the solving of commercial problems. That in my opinion would be a disaster of the first magnitude. I am sure that the university professor who has tasted blood in this war—who has shown himself (quite unlike the popular opinion of the university professor) a man of affairs, an organizer and disciplinarian—I'm afraid that having tasted blood, he may want to stay on that rich food and want to continue to show that he is a first-class investigator and a first-class organizer in industry. It will be nice for him, it will be good for industry, it will be disastrous to the advancement of knowledge.

RABI: I should like to add one remark on this idea of parasites that I gave. This parasite is badly embarrassed. I didn't mean it in any invidious sense.

VEBLEN: Could I say another word in defense of Rabi. I think I know exactly what is back of his remark that it is more comfortable to do research somewhat as a by-product. In any fundamental research you have to take chances. Anyone with experience knows that the chances are you never will do another good job—never again come out with anything really first rate. I remember my old friend Birkhoff saying to me once after a successful feat of research that he felt as if he had come up from a deep dive; he doubted whether he would ever get down to the same depth again. I think that is the problem in the background. And that's why our friends like Mees, in the industrial field, are able to speak so much more enthusiastically about research than we are in the academic field. But, after this has been said, I still don't agree with Rabi that it's a good thing to let research be parasitic on teaching or on other parts of university work. To be so is the traditional American policy, but it isn't necessarily the best policy in the interest of science. We who have grown up in this country ought to recognize, and some of us do recognize although it isn't said publicly as often as it should be, that there has been an enormous difference between our universities and the universities which existed in the last three generations in Europe. The primary function of many European universities was the advancement of knowledge and their secondary function was the dissemination of knowledge. I doubt whether this has been true of more than two or three American universities, and of these universities it has been true only for limited periods of time. It hasn't been, even in our best universities, the rule. I think we ought to give a good deal of our attention to the question whether we can bring about in this country, as well as in other parts of the world, a continuation of the European type of university.

MORRISON: There is a question facing the universities which has only been touched upon and which we should like very much to clear up. It is true that the support that universities have received has been due to their producing of students, and it is in this sense, I suspect, that Rabi made his remark that research was parasitic on teaching. But there seems of late to be a rather similar relationship between university research and war. There are two reasons for this. First, the nuclear physics of today, needing as it does large machines and expensive installations, *needs* support. A great deal of such support is now coming from the Office of Naval Research and will continue to come from that and similar agencies. In some particular cases as much as sixty-five per cent of the work is supported by one or the other of these agencies. Universities cannot construct these tremendous facilities and so such support seems necessary for the progress of physics. Another important reason comes from the military side and can be exemplified by a statement made by Major General Norstadt, who said that hitherto the military has been chiefly interested in special projects, but now it recognizes that that attitude is too narrow, and the army is interested in exploring whole fields of knowledge. The question is, then, whether the natural outcome of this need on the part of research for support and of the desire on the part of the military to give this support is unavoidable. That is, are we destined to see a development of this close relation between nuclear physics and war?

UREY: I want to bring together a couple of remarks that were made by Rabi and Mees. Mees says that if our scientific work in the universities should disappear it would be a tragedy. I agree with that. Rabi pointed out that the government is using at the present time the most efficient way of bringing science in the universities under the domination of the government—namely, farming out large sums of money to the universities until they become used to it. Perhaps in our experience in dealing with the government in all its various forms we have not seen clearly the danger which Rabi has pointed out.

I think that there is a strong possibility that funds for university research will come mainly from the government. If that is to be the case, what mechanism is there by means of which we might avoid complete domination by the government which, I am afraid, is now doing more or less what Mees is afraid of? If only we do not have unification of the armed services, if we have an army and a navy which are separate and keep the traditional enmity between these two services, we may be in a position to escape this domination by playing one against the other. And if it should be possible to get a national science foundation established and to produce rivalry between that national science foundation and both the services, perhaps we should still be able to maintain our independence.

KISTIAKOWSKY: It seems to me that the danger is not in the government offering large sums of money to the colleges, but in the eagerness with which a great many scientists accept this money and sacrifice their freedom—accepting, as they do, a specified program of research. This will make fundamental research suffer and will lead to a continuation of war research under a different guise. If we would just be a little more independent and refuse to accept this money unless it is offered on our own terms, there would not be so much danger as at present is foreseen.

TURNER: There is another aspect of this matter which should be pointed out, the aspect of time scale. It takes quite a while for the consequences of fundamental discoveries to develop, and it is a striking fact that many of our largest industries are based on what were the impractical efforts of impractical men. The time scale of our thinking must be changed to enable us to appreciate fundamental research. The truly fundamental results often crop up more or less accidentally.

Take Veblen's point that research is a gambling proposition: you can hardly expect large corporations to spend much time on the sort of research that can have practical consequences only in the far distant future. The directors have a responsibility to see that the activities are a benefit to the stockholders sooner or later, meaning in effect the lifetime of a man. They can't and don't count on the benefits to the great-grandchildren of the stockholders. Who is supposed to do this kind of research? Universities do it at the present time, but as Condon said, the government laboratories also have a responsibility to the public welfare; and they ought to sponsor this sort of research. Of course, we know that this is now impossible because we don't have an informed public which understands the nature of research or knows how to bring up the goose that is going to lay the golden egg in the course of time.

DuBRIDGE: I come from an institution where research and teaching are carried on at the same time. I have tried to maintain the position that both research and teaching are essential to modern university and engineering schools. I don't think that research can continue to function at full efficiency unless it is stimulated by young students who can furnish new ideas and by their questions can force the research man to restate his ideas in an elementary way. This process stimulates the research man himself as well as the student, and so I would rather replace the word "parasitic" with the word "coordinated" in order to imply that both research and teaching are essential to our modern university.

I emphasize also the point which Kistiakowsky brought

out, namely, that it is of the utmost importance to universities to maintain independence in their acceptance of federal aid for their research. I do not believe that sources of private funds have been completely depleted. It is possible that in the next two or three years they will be, but at the present time this is not the case. And it is of the utmost importance that universities and technical schools secure the largest amount of private support that they can. If they do not, then when the chips are on the table they will find that they are drawing from the government funds to support their own work. If they are also well supplied with their own chips, their decisions can be independent and not be bought by additional support secured from the government. Finally, I would like to reassure Mees about the last point he made, about the danger that those of us who were connected with war laboratories may want to continue in such work. The tendency of many of us has been precisely the opposite; we have been glad to get back to university work and research. Many have, of course, been converted to commercial positions, but for the most part the men engaged in war laboratories are very glad to get back to the university type of work. Some are finding reconversion rather difficult, but not any more than the industries are. The industrial laboratories are not going to claim a large share of the type of research man that belongs in the university.

MEES: I didn't mean I was afraid that the university professors would go on with war research at the present time. I meant that I was afraid that the industries might persuade too many universities to be doing industrial research at the present time, and this would weaken their fundamental research position. There are a number of universities that are continually inviting industrial research to be done in their laboratories. I think that this trend is bad for the future of this country.

HULL: I ought to point out exceptions to Rabi's indictment that industrial laboratories only receive and don't give. The General Electric Research Laboratory has had no difficulty over thirty years in keeping its doors wide open, as most of you know; and also it found no difficulty in obtaining permission for open discussion of scientific work. Exceptions may become the rule, and I think that this one can. It is however contingent on continuation of one fundamental requirement, that is, our patent system. There is a feeling abroad that patents are bad. I feel bound to point out that the one requirement for complete openness in discussion of new scientific results is some sort of protection, not for the scientist who makes the discovery but for the company that wishes to undertake the enormous expense of the development. It should be well understood that that is the fundamental justification for a patent system. If we have a strong patent system, and that is now endangered, there is no reason why any laboratory of which the product is of a patentable nature should not disclose everything that it's doing. They have everything to gain by it, nothing to lose. In the thirty years I have been with General Electric I haven't known of a single case where we have lost by publication or even by telling, in its preliminary stages, what we were doing.

ECKERT: I am associated with the research work of the International Business Machines Corporation. For twenty-five years the corporation has been cooperating with the universities. Scholars in different sciences have come with requests for help on research programs, some sort of laboratory has been established, and the research carried out under the scholars who originated the requests. About twenty years ago I went to the company and suggested that they build a laboratory for completely automatic calculations. The laboratory was established and the control was handed over to a group of which the majority was outside of the company, the Astronomical Society and Columbia University, the company having but one representative. For ten years research was carried on there for the benefit of astronomers, and the company representative came to the laboratory about once a year. There have been many other examples of laboratory establishments: one at California Institute of Technology in connection with the cooperative wind tunnel, one at Harvard with the Sequence Calculator, and many others. Recently the company has embarked on a new program with the creation of the Department of Pure Science for the purpose of effecting cooperation with scholars. The first activity of the department was to establish a new laboratory based on the assumption that there will be cooperation. This expectation comes from several sources. One is that Columbia University invited us to occupy a university building. We have no lease; we are there by invitation only. The university has offered us all its facilities. We have invited scholars from many institutions to come to the laboratory and use its facilities for their own problems. Any member of this conference would be welcome to come there and spend as much time as he wished, and to have his laborious calculations performed for him. The results would of course be public property. The only stipulations are that the results must be of value to science and must be made generally available.

SUITS: I would like to say a few words about this matter of science being parasitic. Several people have referred to this point already; I don't agree with Dr. Rabi in this matter. That industry is parasitic on research would be a far more realistic interpretation of this relationship. My part in this discussion is not to point this out, however, but to examine possible ways in which cooperation might develop among these three types of institutions in our country. As many of you know, I have a very sincere interest in the cooperation among industrial laboratories, university laboratories, and government laboratories. It seems to me that we had a wonderful opportunity during the war to develop this cooperation in a way which it would be quite difficult to accomplish in peacetime. I hope that in the future we will find ways to increase this cooperation.

There has not been enough discussion here of this matter of patents, and in particular on the way it bears on this question. I would feel very sorry if there remained in your minds the impression that patents are a serious difficulty standing in the way of cooperation between industrial and university laboratories, when as a matter of fact the opposite is true. Most industries take out patents on the work they have originated. They will certainly have to continue that in the future for fundamental reasons which Hull has described so well. However, beyond the freedom of further disclosure which the filing of a patent application makes possible to the inventor, there is the realization among industrial scientists that at least as important as the patent is the "know-how" which was developed in the course of work leading to the patent. This fact further minimizes the importance of the patent as a bar to university-industrial scientific collaboration.

In the early stages of industrial development in this country there were possibly many patents which in themselves gave the specifications of a device or product in such detail that from these patents one could go ahead and build this device or product. With the highly technical patents of importance to industry today, this is not usually the case. I have seen the attempts made recently to construct from the teachings of a patent, let us say, a vacuum tube, or a chemical process. It is a matter of the greatest difficulty to take a patent and from it build the device which the patent describes. I think that in the future this will be more true because of the increasing complexity of technical development. Devices and products are becoming more and more complicated; many people are involved in the development procedure, and large devices and complex instrumentations are frequently employed. As a practical matter, the important thing to an industry is not only that this patent is in its files but that within its organization there are some people who know how to do what the patent describes. Consider, for example, the problem of setting up a chemical pilot plant. It would be remarkable if that could be done from a patent describing the process. What you have to do is find the engineer or scientist who talked with the patent attorney but who could not possibly impart to him all that he knew about the invention.

At General Electric the patent system certainly hasn't been a bar to cooperation with other laboratories. At least if it has, we in the laboratories are certainly not aware of it.

HAWKINS: My interest in nuclear physics is that of an observer of nuclear physicists. I wish to discuss our problem by going back to the position of the research worker as a member of a university, whose functions include those of being an operating part of our economy and our society, but also that of being its critic. It has been said by several people that the situation with which nuclear research is confronted is that of being absorbed into the working economy, of being made non-parasitic, both in military research and in industrial research. In military research it has become clear that qualitative improvements in weapons are much more important than they were previously thought to be. If there are wars in the future, they will depend more and more on the technology of nations and on its rate of growth, rather than upon manpower or industrial potential *per se*. This is perhaps an exaggeration for the immediate future, but certainly not in the long run.

Similarly in our industrial system; its growth is no longer so directly dependent upon the growth of manpower, nor upon the increasing mechanical division of labor in industry; it is increasingly dependent upon the development of new technologies, and particularly upon their rate of growth. In this new situation it will be difficult for the scientist to avoid being drawn into spending more and more of his time on this new function of science. How is he to avoid neglecting the basic aspects of science?

Several suggestions have been made—for example, the possibility of playing the Army and Navy against each other and private funds against each of these, and also even the possibility that a third government agency might increase the chances of the scientists for getting out of this wall which is surrounding them. I raise the question: why should we not become non-parasitic, why not be absorbed either in military technology or industrial development? There are a great many subtle points in this question. It is very difficult to draw a line between fundamental science and applied science. Nuclear physics has reached a point where it must get new data; there is little likelihood of great advance from the purely theoretical side. Advance will require more data, and it is going to be very expensive. I find it somewhat difficult to believe that it is possible to get this financial support without becoming involved in the trap. But again, what is the trap? I suggest that in the case of universities, the scientific research worker has obligations to his university as a general social being and social critic. I think that the feeling which is implicit in the minds of many people, although they may not perhaps express it, is that they will in some sense cease to be free members of the university as society's critic, that they will lose their economically parasitic position and also their socially free position as members of society whose responsibility it is to say where we are going and why.

VALLARTA: The time has come all over the world when money in large sums is being appropriated from public funds for scientific work. In this connection attempts are being made to justify the expenditure of such funds in terms of patentable results which are obtained through the expenditure of the funds. This is entirely wrong. I consider it the duty of the scientists in every country to make sure that the people who are administering public funds for scientific research assign these funds without regard to whether or not they will produce any practical results. In Mexico we have made sure that no question of practical results is involved in the assignment of any funds for scientific research. This brings me to my second remark, which is about patents. To our mind, any patent law which does not protect the inventor has very little justification for its existence.

CORYELL: I would like to refer again to the remark that research is parasitic on the university. It seems to me that the military divisions of our country are parasitic on technology, and thus are the military parts of society now invading the university. The question of greatest importance, I think, is the relation which exists between society as such and universities as such. The universities should feel more responsibility for the needs of society than they usually do, and fulfill more of the needs of the people; if they do, the recent threat will vanish, and we shall eliminate in ten, twenty, or fifty years the problems which have been bothering many of us here.

K. T. COMPTON: Some of the problems that we face in dealing with the government are, I think, capable of solution. Certainly, the relationship between government and private research agencies is proper and can be mutually beneficial, and in some cases, for example in nuclear research where large sums of money are required, it seems essential for the furtherance of the art. What are some of the hurdles? I have in my files a letter which unfortunately I can't publish, although I have wanted to on several occasions, from a former government official. I can quote this almost verbatim: "The trouble with American scientists is that they are emotionally unstable and don't understand the first principles of democracy. I notice that when federal funds are available they line up at the trough; I think they will continue to do so." I think we should see by contrast the agencies which have developed an increasing understanding of the problems of science in the universities and industry during the war. I believe we are making an earnest effort to set up agencies for research programs that will be mutually beneficial and proper for all concerned. Just to mention one, I think that the Office of Naval Research is making a very sincere effort in that respect. One thing I think we could do is to aid and support the one type of group, and not support the other.

In attempting to support the groups that are doing a good job, there is one difficulty which I know some of us have run up against. It is not due to the officers or officials in charge of the program; they have the best ideas in the world as to how it should be carried out. The contracts are drawn up in a satisfactory way; but when we come to deal with the government fiscal agents, the contract agents, then we have a different proposition. They are a different group, they are not concerned with our problems, they are not concerned with the problems of research, they are concerned only with making the best bargain they can for the government. I think the universities are very much handicapped in dealing with this group because we are not skilled in their art; we haven't had to fight that kind of battle for some time. I think the industries are in a better position than the universities. In the cases where the university has been tough about these matters, the terms have been, on the whole, good. The university research worker should realize that he is in a seller's market; he has something to sell that is wanted. I think some of these practical difficulties can be met if the scientist who deals with these agencies and the institutions that deal with these agencies stand firmly on high principles and don't begin to compromise for the sake of getting funds easily. It seems to me that unless we stand firm, we are in difficulty.

I want to point out one more problem that concerns some of us more than the problem of patents. That is the question of overhead available on these contracts. During the war, institutions were anxious to be helpful and do a job. I think there were in many cases contracts which would be highly impractical and even detrimental to the university if they were in effect in peacetime. These institutions are now in the position of trying to get together and work out a rational solution that will be practical and fair all around. I think this is an example of one of the ways in which we can not only defend what we think is right in our operations, but also educate and get precedents set with the government.

RABI: In my opening remarks, I spoke of *university* research, and I meant university research in the sense of a scholar working with his students, both in the development of knowledge and the development of those students. I did not refer to a research institution, even to such as are connected with universities. Such an institution is in an entirely different category, being specifically for research. It is not the university *per se*, though under a common administration.

One other remark with regard to small scale research and getting ahead fast. My views are rather conservative; I think that science is infinite—we are not going to exhaust it by gathering more facts faster. I think it is a way of life; the way one goes at the task has important cultural and aesthetic values which are at least as important as the quantity of scientific results. I am afraid that in our efforts to organize expensive scientific experiments, the other more tender plant may be lost.

THE LARGE LABORATORY
IN NUCLEAR RESEARCH

L. A. DUBRIDGE

I THINK I should start out by warning anyone who is
expecting definite answers to the many questions concerning the place large laboratories are going to play in
physics research that he will be disappointed. My objective
will be to ask questions more than to answer them.

In the past, basic research in physics has been carried on
primarily in small laboratories. A research worker with a
few assistants was the fundamental unit. It is true that in the
larger universities and some industries a number of these
research units were assembled under one roof and under one
department chairman. The units themselves, however, were
reasonably independent, though the stimulation brought
about by many units working near each other was of the
greatest importance.

Now there were individual cases, of course, usually under
the leadership of a great research figure such as a Rutherford
or a Kammerlingh Onnes where the individual research
units combined efforts in a cooperative attack on some major
problem or field. Some of these were eminently successful.
Even in them, however, independence of the individual
units was the rule. Each unit built up its own equipment
and facilities. In some instances the units shared some major
piece of equipment with others, such as in the famous Leyden cryogenic laboratory.

Such was the picture before 1930 in basic physics, even the
basic physics carried on in industrial laboratories.

In applied science the situation was quite different. In
many large industrial laboratories concentrated cooperative

attacks on important problems have been organized with conspicuous success. The various aspects of the problem were parcelled out to specialized groups, each of which was responsible for the development required to bring its unit in line with the whole.

The beginnings of a change in the organization of basic science laboratories began with the development and perfection of the cyclotron as a research tool. Here was a major piece of equipment which could keep many individual research units busy. Several problems could be carried on in parallel, and the combined efforts of all groups were needed to keep the machine in operation and to carry on continued improvements. In a sense then, the large laboratory of the sort I am referring to began with the Radiation Laboratory of the University of California. Other smaller groups, built on a similar pattern, grew up in other parts of the country, and cooperative research had become a reality by the time the war broke out.

The war brought about the greatest flowering of large cooperative laboratories in history. Laboratories numbering many hundreds or even several thousand employees grew up for the development of radar, proximity fuses, nuclear energy, and other fields. Their achievements were so astounding that they at once raised the question of why peacetime research could not be carried out in the same way. This is the question which I would like to examine in more detail. There is danger of misreading the lessons taught by the war, but there is also the danger of not reading these lessons at all.

In the first place it is necessary to emphasize the fact that these huge war laboratories were not research laboratories in the sense that they carried on research in pure physics. They were applied physics laboratories; they were built and organized to develop specific weapons of war. The basic research which paves the way had been done before the war.

The tools were for the most part at hand; they had only to be put into usable form. True, many basic problems had to be examined or reexamined, but these researches were for the most part incidental to the task of developing a weapon. These laboratories followed in many respects the patterns which had already been set by the industrial laboratories in attacking applied problems. But they went further in size, in the degree of specialization of the groups, and in the number of scientists employed.

We cannot, however, conclude that because these laboratories succeeded in their technological job, they could also be adapted to the problems of basic research. Nor can we conclude the opposite.

A second feature of these laboratories was that they were built up under conditions peculiar to a war, conditions which cannot possibly be reproduced in time of peace. During the war it was possible to drain the colleges and universities of scientists to man the laboratories. This produced serious enough results during the war; it would be impossible and disastrous in time of peace. Nevertheless, more scientists can be trained; so the availability of enough scientists need be no permanent or insurmountable obstacle to large laboratories if they are needed.

Still more important, in fact the dominating feature in any laboratory problem, is the attitude of the scientists themselves. During the war they were willing to live and work under necessarily unsatisfactory conditions. They were willing to be regimented (at least most of them were) for the common good. They were willing to engage in all sorts of tasks—tedious and uninteresting ones, field work, even administrative work—which were far afield from their interests as research workers. In short they were willing to give up the most cherished privileges normally associated with scientific work—independence and freedom. They were not only willing but anxious to give up these things because the

incentives were so overpowering. The opportunity of helping in a significant way to win the war reduced all other
considerations to insignificance. I believe no other objective,
no matter how fine it might be, can provide the tremendous
emotional stimulus to collaborative effort which the war
supplied. Without this stimulus any laboratory built along
lines of the great war laboratories is bound to collapse, just
as every single war laboratory collapsed whether it wished
to or not soon after the war ended.

Our lesson from the war experience is that great laboratories can be successful in the field of applied science in
time of war. One can safely predict that any attempt to keep
going into peacetime a laboratory built up during the war for
war purposes is doomed to failure, whether it be operated
under civilian or military control. If great laboratories are
needed in time of peace, they must be built for peacetime
conditions.

The first question is whether, in the field of basic science,
there is a need for something more than the individual
laboratory of pre-war days. Let me emphasize again the
words "basic science." I am not talking about applied science,
about industrial laboratories, or about military laboratories
for defense purposes. There is no doubt a need for such
laboratories; they can be successful if conditions are
right. What these conditions are, I will come to in a moment.

But let us now ask whether in the field of nuclear physics
there are reasons for establishing large laboratories. I believe
there are; and the reason is simple. Some of the facilities required for modern work in nuclear physics are so large and
so expensive that a large staff is required to operate and make
full use of them, and only a few such major facilities can be
built in this country.

I have no doubt that small nuclear reactors and small or
medium sized accelerators will some day be found in al-

most every well-equipped physics research laboratory. But the huge high-power pile, the billion-volt accelerator will for some years to come be found only in a few places. It will be poor economy to build such facilities and not have available the large research and technical staff required to use them to full capacity, and it will be equally tragic if such facilities are not open to use by physicists throughout the country. I believe it is inevitable that a few great research centers will grow up, and that they will be of greatest importance in the advance of nuclear physics.

Such laboratories might be sponsored and managed either by a single university, by an industrial corporation, a government agency, or an independent non-profit corporation organized for the purpose.

I think it is evident that neither an industry nor a government agency is suited to manage a laboratory built largely for basic research. Industry must ultimately seek a practical goal; government or military agencies are not set up to operate basic research.

There is no doubt that any one of a dozen major universities or engineering schools could operate a major nuclear physics center. The University of California at Berkeley is now doing it. The commanding position of this university on the Pacific Coast, the eminence of Lawrence and his staff of the Radiation Laboratory, and the warm welcome which visitors and workers from other institutions have always had, assure the success of this great center. This laboratory satisfies all the conditions which we shall name presently.

But Berkeley is in a unique position. It is unlikely that the pattern established there can be followed elsewhere in the country. In the East there are many great institutions within easy reach of each other. Since it must be government funds which finance such a laboratory, it will be difficult to pick one institution to operate it, and even then full use by other groups is not easy to ensure. At any rate in two cases, Chicago and the Northeast, the universities themselves have preferred cooperative management. The question of the place and success of large cooperative laboratories will soon have an experimental answer.

Without presuming to tell these laboratories how they should set themselves up, it may still be worthwhile to set forth some of the conditions which any such laboratory must meet to avoid known pitfalls.

It should be clear that independent laboratories will have as their major facilities only those very large installations which are beyond what a single university could contemplate operating, or which, because of shortage of material or funds, not more than one or two universities in any area could have. Such laboratories should not compete with or duplicate or take the place of strong university physics departments. Rather, like a 200-inch telescope, they should provide facilities of an extraordinary type for use by many people.

As to location, there are many difficult problems to be met. Physical facilities such as power, water, isolation to avoid radiation dangers, etc. must all be considered. But less tangible elements may be even more important. To attract a permanent staff they must provide a satisfactory place to live. This means convenience to a metropolitan area with its housing, shopping, educational and cultural advantages. Desert isolation is no drawing card for most physicists. Living conditions must be positively attractive if the highest quality temporary or permanent staff are to be drawn in.

Location near one or more strong universities is also important. Nothing can replace the close ties to the atmosphere, libraries, contacts with students and other scientific companionship and other attributes of a university. What geographical separation is necessary can be partially bridged by official university connections so that ties with the academic world are real.

It is evident that the establishment must not only have an adequate maintenance, technical, clerical, and engineering staff, but also a permanent or semi-permanent scientific staff of high quality supervising its general program. And this permanent staff must attract and welcome other workers who come in for short or long periods. The laboratory should offer opportunities for many young men to come in on post-doctorate fellowships to complete their training and acquire research experience. One of its important contributions to physics will be its training of young men.

The permanent staff will need to map out the general important lines of effort, but the program must be flexible enough to make room for new ideas and new lines of attack which either the permanent or visiting staff wish to carry out. Wartime regimentation can have no part in a successful basic research establishment.

All of these are obvious statements, but they are no less important for that, for the obvious is frequently most easily overlooked. Furthermore, these are conditions which can be readily met by intelligent management. If progress in nuclear physics is important to the nation, to the world, and to science itself, it is important that they must be met. The cognizant government and military agencies must recognize that these are not whims of crazy scientists but are part of the necessary fabric of the atmosphere in which science flourishes.

That these new laboratories will face grave difficulties, no one questions. They may not succeed. For the next few years the shortage of scientific personnel may prevent their adequate development or slow it down. There are not enough physicists at the present moment to man all our current ambitious programs, but our physics departments are all but clogged with ambitious and able graduate students. They will soon be flowing out to fill the critical gaps. We all witnessed what young men could do during the war; they will do it again.

I look forward with keen interest to a great new experiment in physics research. Those who long for the old days with the lone worker in the basement room with his wax and string and glassblowing torch can have them. I believe that the essential spirit of the old days—freedom of inquiry, time for thought—can be obtained even in the pressure of great new physical and organizational techniques. I shall leave it to the fortunate leaders of these great new establishments to justify our optimism.

DISCUSSION

THOMAS: I would like to emphasize two points for your consideration. The first of these concerns the psychological attitude of the scientist, his feelings toward his work in these large government institutions. I have found that the scientist wants to have a definite part in the running of the institution in which he works. He wants to know what questions are being considered, and he wants to have something to say about how matters of policy are decided. This is an admirable feeling. In a large government laboratory the chances for self-expression are rather limited. Everything is run according to form. There is a set procedure for practically every movement the workers make, and in this maze of red tape it is impossible to attain any freedom of action. How, then, can the scientist best be made to feel himself an integral part of the organization? This condition is accentuated when, as so often is the case, a government scientist is doing a considerable amount of moving around within the various departments of a laboratory, or from laboratory to laboratory. This makes him feel like a transient. Indeed, there are several aspects to this all-important psychological problem.

The second point on which I would like to encourage discussion is the matter of money and its effects. Never before in the history of science has there been so much money available for research as there is at present. It has reached the stage where practically any good idea may be immediately subsidized and put to work. Is it possible that perhaps we have too much money for our own good? Is it so easy to obtain money for buildings and equipment that our judgment will be warped into approving large expenditures without due prior reflection and consideration? It may well be that this has already occurred in the past to slow down the overall progress of science.

The whole process of setting up these large laboratories is essentially an experiment in a new and untried field. It may be that in another ten years we will know the answers to these questions that I raise, and then we will be able to judge with what wisdom we are attacking the problems today. It seems to me that our task in these next ten years will be primarily that of guiding our course by careful coordination of the old with the new.

MEES: When DuBridge started to discuss this I was reminded of Kipling's poem, "MacAndrew's Hymn," which concerns the future of the steam engine, and goes in part: "I hae no doubt for the machine but what about the man?" When you talk about a large laboratory you are talking about the shadow of a man. All the examples that you gave were shadows of men. If you can find a Rutherford, if you can find an E. O. Lawrence, there will be no difficulty about those laboratories; they will be tremendous successes. But if you build a laboratory and then go looking for a man you will have a series of disappointments and heartaches, when you find you have mistaken the man. It seems to me that the only way these big laboratories can be built is in the shadow of a man. Get your man first, watch him grow as a young man, give him the facilities that he wants as the Rockefeller Foundation did for E. O. Lawrence, let him build up his staff and his organization and let him go on as far as it will take him. By that time he should have been able to train his successors and you will have your big laboratory. Remember Hale at Mount Wilson, for instance. He started a laboratory first at Yerkes Observatory and proved himself a great leader of astronomical research. He got a 60-inch telescope at Mount Wilson, and after that had been proved a triumphant success he got the 100-inch telescope, and then he embarked on the heartbreaking job of the 200-inch. His health unfortunately failed before it was finished. Hale was followed by Adams, and so far Mount Wilson has been the reflection of Hale and Adams. If we get more Hales and more Adamses we can have more great observatories. I should hate to build a laboratory or a series of laboratories and then try to find the people to run them, as is being done now.

DuBridge: Mees' point is well taken, and he has stated what I think may in the future be the stumbling block for these laboratories. My hope springs from the fact that several times during the war we saw a need and created a project and did succeed, in some cases at least, in finding a leader, for example Los Alamos with Oppenheimer; and there is hope that there are enough men to grow with these positions and make them successful.

Blackett: There is one point made by DuBridge which I would like to take up. One cannot and should not expect governments to run fundamental research. This must be run by the scientists themselves. In the past fundamental research has run itself; that is, there has been no central direction needed and decisions and initiative were local in character with financial resources obtained mainly from private benefactors. Now that fundamental research has increased so much in scale and expense, and the deliberate, and in my view, correct taxation policy in England has made reliance on private benefactors impossible, it is clearly necessary for the state to provide the necessary funds. The important question is: "How are they to be provided?" In my view, it is most important that they should (a) be provided through the mechanism of a civil not a military department, (b) be allocated on the advice of the scientists themselves, acting through a system of advisory committees. This is more or less the arrangement which is growing up in England. I am opposed to a British university taking research contracts from a military department in peacetime, if it can possibly be avoided.

POLANYI: Veblen reminded us of the fact that some of the great academic institutions of the world existed on the European continent, and probably he was speaking of Germany. There a great many institutions were supported by the government and yet maintained complete academic freedom. In particular I should like to mention in this connection the Kaiser Wilhelm Institute, with which I had the honor to be associated for ten years in earlier days. That institution after the last war was entirely supported by government funds. It was built, in what Mees regards as being the correct way, by finding a man and building a laboratory around him. It was in fact not the government that was directing the institution, but it was the opinion of the scientists themselves that ran it. The independence of that opinion was based on reason, and to some extent, on constitutional safeguards. I think that it is not so much the administration which determines the function of the institution, but rather a public opinion which has respect for certain forms of freedom, which has respect in this case for the autonomous opinions of science and which watches the freedom of those who are charged with scientific work. When that public opinion is properly cultivated, the form of the support whether state or private, will matter little, for the respect will be there and the safeguards will be there in consequence.

IRENE CURIE-JOLIOT: Speaking for my husband as well as for myself, I should like to mention the situation of research in France. We have an organization something like that first set up by Cockcroft. In this system, government funds are given to a Center of Scientific Research, of which my husband was director last year. These funds are then given out to various laboratories for research requiring special apparatus and so forth. They are also distributed for the purpose of scholarships and research among individuals. The Center of Scientific Research now has some laboratories of its own. There is a director, but the distribution of these funds is not decided by the director alone; there are scientific committees for the distribution of the funds. Such a committee is composed of men who have constant contact with the universities and various research laboratories. The system is very elastic and has achieved many good results from research programs in universities and research laboratories comparable to those already discussed here. The spirit of the committee in its relations with these laboratories is very much like the spirit of a university. We believe that this is a good solution.

DANIELS: One of the laboratories that DuBridge referred to, the Argonne National Laboratory, has been operating for three months and some of the problems might be worth discussing here. That laboratory was set up in cooperation with twenty-five universities in the Middle West, the idea being that the facilities of this government laboratory should be spread around among universities and taxpayers. Important also was the idea that government laboratories sometimes get into ruts, and that it is a good idea to have a constant stream of fresh scientists from universities going through these laboratories.

If the visiting scientists stay a year, they can do a lot. But what about a short period of three months, for example? That may be hardly enough time for them to get acquainted. Our experience has borne out the fact that a man with experience in nuclear physics, having available the full facilities of the laboratory, can accomplish a lot in three months. Some very important work has already been done by scientists coming from universities, some of them even for periods as short as three months.

It has been suggested that laboratories of this kind should not compete with the universities in the matter of research. Now this is a proper point of view, yet it is very difficult to carry out. You'll find that if you interpret the rule too strictly, you won't keep your best scientists in the government laboratory. A real researcher must be free to go wherever his research leads him, and we found immediately that if we are going to restrict the laboratory research to that which could not be done in the universities, we would lose our men. So, as a general principle, I would say, "Let the research men on the permanent staff of the government laboratory plan to build and use piles and do other things which the universities can't do, but don't restrict them too much." If they are studying fission products and want to determine the magnetic moment of these products, they should be free to do it. If you say, "No, that's got to be done in the universities," you soon won't have a strong laboratory.

Thomas's point is an excellent one. You must give all the laboratory scientists a voice in running the laboratory. The government is going to set some of the patterns and objectives, but the details must be worked out by the laboratory staff. A laboratory council may well pass on some of the important administrative problems.

The twenty-five universities have elected a board of governors which shapes the policy of the Argonne National

Laboratory. The bills have been paid by the Manhattan District and presumably will be paid by the Atomic Energy Commission. But it is a closely cooperating institution. We have a contractor, the University of Chicago, which is advised by the board of governors, which in turn is elected by the representatives of the twenty-five universities. Some of the problems involve liabilities and responsibility for accidents. To solve these we have insisted, so far, that everyone who comes to work in the laboratory shall be on the payroll of the Argonne Laboratory. Even if it's nothing a year, nevertheless he is an employee of the contractor. Of course he may still be a member of his own university. Regarding health problems, the visiting scientists are treated exactly the same as the regular staff; they are given the same medical examinations. Regarding publication, if a man comes from a university to work at this large government laboratory and draws his salary from the university, he will publish from the university and the Argonne National Laboratory. If he chooses to draw his pay from the National Laboratory (and perhaps most of them will) and works on a problem of interest to the National Laboratory, then he will publish from the government laboratory and his university.

The program seems to be working out very well. I'm sure that we can look forward to successful operation of this large government laboratory cooperating with the surrounding universities.

ROBERTSON: We have heard from representatives of Britain, France and Mexico on the ways in which they at present are meeting this problem of the support of research. Daniels has discussed the particular research laboratory which is under subfranchise from our own government. I feel that in these discussions not enough has been said concerning the long-range goal of the attitude of the government toward research. Mention was made of the Assistant Chief of Staff existing for research and development in the

Army; similarly in the Air Force there has been formed a Deputy Chief of Air Staff. Mention was also made by Karl Compton of the functions of the Office of Research and Invention, now the Office of Naval Research, in the Navy. I think that we should realize that this recognition of the necessity for strengthening research and development within the service forces is a different problem from that of making available for general research a fund on a scale large enough to support large laboratories. The war has shown the necessity for the services, and other government branches which have specific duties, to get more into the scientific field; and I feel that the requirement of these offices in our service forces has more to do with the making of products for their particular purpose than with the general problem of the long-range greater utilization of our research facilities for the betterment of the living conditions and the general welfare of mankind. It seems to me that the kind of solution which Britain and France have been offering is along the line of what we should like to see developed —namely, recognition of the desirability of having research for its own sake, not with any particular end in mind at the moment. I think it not quite proper to look upon the services as being the ones to fulfill that aim under a subterfuge. The Office of Naval Research is certainly a very excellent temporary expedient for taking on the sponsorship of fairly pure scientific research. But in so far as the aim of its contracts does not lead directly to security, there will sooner or later be an accounting, and it will become necessary to reorient the program in order to achieve the economy which will be demanded. I hope for the time when we shall have some particular civilian institution in the government responsible for the advancement of knowledge. If we are justified in our claims concerning the value of research to mankind as a whole, it should be recognized by a particular civilian agency to be charged with the advancement of research without any specific purpose, such as security. In this way the problem of the large laboratory conducting pure research would be solved.

DuBRIDGE: I would like to support Robertson's contention strongly. One of the reasons for the present confusion is simply that our government has no policy in regard to a research program. The people in the Office of Naval Research, for example, admit quite freely, and in fact insist upon the point, that they do not intend and are not able to support scientific research indefinitely. They are not set up for that purpose, and that isn't the function of the Navy. They are doing this only as a stop-gap, while federal policy is being discussed and formulated, with the idea that eventually there will be a science foundation or something of that sort specifically set up for basic research, and many of the things which they are now supporting will be passed over to the science foundation. We may have a difference of opinion as to whether this will really happen or not, but I think that these who are in the Office of Naval Research sincerely believe that this is the case and that they are merely supporting science in the interim. I think it is a great tragedy that a science foundation of one kind or another failed of adoption by the last Congress. What is badly needed is for our Congress to formulate a definite policy and to create a civilian agency to carry it out.

ALLISON: I think that one of the aspects of our government which among others must be bewildering to some of our foreign guests is the fact that although everyone in this country believes that education is a major concern, there is no Secretary of Education in the federal government and no Department of Education. The kind of research that I like to do, the kind of research I have done, is intimately associated with education. I am used to working with a few graduate students in a laboratory and considering the research that we do as consisting both of finding out the properties of matter and also as part of their training. It seems to me that perhaps this educational kind of research will remain fundamentally free longer than any other. This is probably not the fastest way to find out the fundamental facts about some particular part of the universe; it is probably much faster to get together a high-powered team of mature men and go after it. But the kind of research I like, the kind that I have done, has been in connection with education; and I consider it desirable to have this connection.

CONDON: I think that we should not look upon the National Science Foundation as a dead issue. After all, the bill did pass the Senate and might have passed the House but for the approach of the end of the session. I approve of the idea of a science foundation, and I think that one thing that contributed to its setback was the fact that everybody was well taken care of without it. The Army and Navy money was so plentiful that there wasn't any very strong incentive to press the bill. Everybody was so busy getting contracts that they didn't have enough time to put pressure on Congress. Maybe that means that just as soon as the Army-Navy money runs out we shall have a science foundation.

UREY: It is by no means to be assumed that the most important discoveries have been made in large laboratories. Most of them were made with limited facilities. The discovery of the meson, the positron, the neutron, artificial radioactivity—all these were made in laboratories with very limited facilities. I ask this question in connection with our large laboratories—will it come about that a large number of our most brilliant young men spend their time on engineering, when they should have time to think and study and perhaps to lead us on in important directions? It seems to me that this possible disadvantage of mass-production research is a very serious one.

DUBRIDGE: If I gave the impression of differing from

what Urey has just said, I did not make myself clear. I agree
with him wholeheartedly. He has given one of the reasons
why these large laboratories will not compete dangerously
with the universities. At the same time, there are many
basic questions which we can't investigate without complicated facilities. We can't look into the reactions of high-
energy gamma-rays until we have the gamma-rays. Yet many
discoveries will undoubtedly be made in small laboratories
without large facilities.

K. T. COMPTON: In the early 1920's, just after World
War I, when we discovered the great advances that had been
made in Germany, for example in quantum theory, I sometimes wondered whether great theoretical advances were not
sometimes stimulated by inability to get one's hands on apparatus and the consequent necessity of simply thinking.
Sometimes I think that if we have too many funds available, we build equipment too rapidly and without due reflection. I would like to read to you a paragraph of a letter from
W. R. Whitney, then Director of the General Electric Research Laboratory, which he wrote when I had asked him to
give me his spontaneous reactions on certain questions. He
complied in a most interesting fashion, and at the end he
said, "You asked for spontaneous reactions, and these are
certainly spontaneous. If these are too spontaneous for you,
I can probably do better with a little reflection." So probably
can I.

The foregoing remarks are only semi-serious. I do think
that well-equipped laboratories are of importance second
only to genius and training. Laboratory equipment is becoming progressively more important as new research tools
become available and as the frontiers of science are pushed
into regions of greater complexity. Our wartime experience
shows how scientists can multiply their efforts if they have
assistance enough of relatively routine and manual char-

acter. If the leadership of the large laboratories is sound, the large laboratories will be all right.

SHAPLEY: The revival of interest in the proposal of a National Science Foundation is very encouraging. Such a foundation may become largely responsible for our scientific activity. Many details remain to be resolved, and much assistance will be needed in resolving them in the next few months; but all of you here, I hope, are in sympathy with the idea. You have got your ONR and ORI contracts, and should have some spare time now to consider the basis of future support. We all know that this Office of Naval Research is a temporary device, but it helps a great deal. We shall be grateful for it, because there has been such generosity in not demanding specific results. It is chiefly and definitely support of basic science. And we don't feel badly corrupted by our contracts with ONR and ORI.

I want you to realize, though, that our big results in the future are going to come from various sources—from the small basement lone-wolf laboratories and also from the enormous university laboratories. I am thoroughly convinced that a lot of good ideas are going to come from the small laboratories, just as Urey said. That is why I want to emphasize, in our ambitions for a National Science Foundation, the importance of a very wide spread. Some of us are worried about the "pork barrel" part of the National Science Foundation's plan, namely, the distribution of a small percentage, say ten or fifteen per cent, evenly among the states to support basic scientific research. That plan is put in for two reasons. One is to encourage the small institutions, and the other is to get votes in Congress. We ought not to deprecate this policy. If we can support the National Science Foundation with the interest of the small institutions primarily in mind, our policy will feed men and ideas into the large institutions, and in the long run it will pay off. For the present we know that we are going to get more research results per dollar from some of the big institutions and their great concentrations of scientists than we shall from an isolated small college or small university laboratory. But in the long run we would have our young college men trained in the spirit of research. These young men will later do the work in the big institutions. I hope that, if we go on striving for a National Science Foundation, we shall favor the widespread use of funds, partly so that we can get the legislation through, and partly because in the long run it is a good policy.

WIGNER: Since I am at heart a very old-fashioned theoretical physicist, Urey spoke very much from my heart and I very much agree with him. Just the same, I feel sure that the big laboratories are here to stay, because the facilities which are needed for conducting nuclear research are immeasurably greater now than were the facilities needed for research in physics some time ago. It is clear that the large instruments cannot be erected and cannot be well used without a large laboratory. Therefore the question is really, "How can we combine the advantages of the large laboratory with the advantages of people who wish to tackle the problems at least as much by thought as by some new equipment?" The answer was suggested by Daniels, who has pointed out that some very important work has been done at the Argonne Laboratories by people who have been there for only three months. I believe that the solution of the problem is, at least to a large degree, to be found in a rapid turnover of at least part of the personnel of the large laboratories. The main trouble with the large laboratories and the well-established big institutions is that people get too used to each other, too used to each other's modes of thinking, and the sense of adventure may soon evaporate from the whole enterprise. A constantly changing surrounding will alleviate this difficulty. One of the big advantages of the university is that there is always an influx of a new group of ignorant people to whom you have to explain the basis of each idea, and each idea is challenged by them so that you are forced to maintain an intimate contact with the bases of your ideas. You live in a lively atmosphere. In the large laboratories a reasonably rapid turnover of the personnel both at the top and also at the bottom may help to create a similar atmosphere.

UREY: I believe that this problem that I have raised can be solved by administration. It is mostly a matter of recognizing that a problem exists. We have succeeded in our universities largely because of the great freedom which exists in them, the privilege of a person to do what he pleases with nobody to check up on him. He can have his position in the university, and he can go on with whatever kind of work he wishes. There is nobody to regiment him, nobody to put him to work on a particular problem. I believe the problem of the big laboratories can be solved by precisely the same method. All you have to do is recognize that there is a place for people around those laboratories even if they are not busy constructing something all the time but look as if they are complete parasites on the organization. It is not a problem which is unsolvable; it is merely a problem of recognizing that it exists and acting accordingly.

VALLARTA: Of all the various views that have been expressed today, there is one with which I personally find myself in complete sympathy and that is the one which was so ably expressed by Mees at the beginning of the discussion. That point of view is that it does not matter whether we have small or large laboratories; what matters is to find the man, the proper man, around whom the laboratory is to be built. If that man needs an installation which costs a hundred million dollars and needs a staff of several thousand, all right; if that man needs only the laboratory in his own cellar and a few pieces of apparatus, that is what we should provide him with. But I feel very strongly that the essential point is the man.

RUSSELL: May I speak in support of the view of Mees and Vallarta. In forty years experience in astronomy I have watched many groups, watched them grow, watched them decline, and watched them come back; and in every instance, and without mentioning any names, I think I can say that my colleagues in my own profession and I all agree that these advances and these retrogressions had to do more than anything else with the man who directed the group.

BREIT: I do not want to strike a pessimistic note, but I think there is a certain danger that the National Science Foundation will not accomplish its purpose. Now of course if the National Science Foundation will just have contracts with the universities, everything will be fine provided that there are no restrictions to those contracts. At the same time, observing the way our federal research is usually managed in peacetime, I don't think we shall accomplish what this group would like to see; for ordinarily it has been felt that every cent must be accounted for exactly because the taxpayer must know how it has been spent, so that a lot of clerical work is necessitated; there is no freedom for research, and there is often no real advance in knowledge.

DuBRIDGE: It has now been pointed out that there are differences in the problem in various countries. In the United States we have discovered the contract method, which seems to be the way in our country to avoid direct government control with the government actually maintaining and running laboratories. The National Science Foundation was not conceived as an agency to set up a laboratory of its own but as an agency to support the work of the various universities through contracts. This has been our scheme to avoid direct government control of research and ensure the control of research by the scientists. There are many who advocate a fund for the National Academy of Sciences to administer. There are many advantages in such a plan; and the Academy, like the Royal Society, could possibly have done the job. But for various reasons this plan was not adopted.

In conclusion I would like to emphasize that I have confined my attention to the large laboratories. I want to make it very clear that while I think that in nuclear physics there is a place for the large laboratories, I do not think at all that they are destined to exclude all else. The worker in his own individual laboratory and in the ordinary laboratories of universities and colleges will still have a place in the framework of research.

THE USES AND HOPES
OF SCIENTIFIC SOCIETIES

HARLOW SHAPLEY

TO advance on a wide front our science-based modern culture is the primary use of scientific societies. The hope of scientific societies is to accomplish this uniform advance in such a manner that individuals the world over grow in quality as ethical intelligent beings, without loss of personality or serious curbing of personal freedom.

In all the varied fields of science, the assembling of individual practitioners obviously makes both a social and a scientific contribution. Since scientific work is frequently difficult and exacting, and is occasionally little appreciated or little applauded by the public, the social phase of scientific societies is important for the maintenance of morale, and therefore important for the advance of science.

I have tried to find serious objections to the existence and customary operations of scientific societies, but without much success. There is some risk of bureaucratic evils in the management of large societies. Human vanity is nurtured by election to some of the honor societies, with little compensatory gain to science; but the society as a whole, even in such rare instances, is useful if for nothing more than incitation to early and vigorous effort. Domination by scientific brass hats may hinder the effectiveness of some societies, but it does not wholly discourage their existence. Professional neglect by societies of the lone-wolf sort of worker may occasion a little loss now and then, but it is trivial compared with the gains. To sum it up, there seems to be no abundance of objections to the formation and operation of scientific societies.

To speak concretely of the gains of organized societies of scientists, and especially of their hopes in science and in the social order, I shall mention briefly five types of organization, and, speaking for myself only and not for the societies, state my hope for the future development of each. They are:

I. The local science club
II. The national professional society
III. The local and national interscience association of professionals
IV. The international professional unions and congresses
V. The international interscience organizations.

The examples I shall cite are organizations with which I have official connection.

In the secondary schools of America there are thousands of science clubs. They are composed of science students working under the sponsorship of a teacher or some other local leader. Many deal with science in general, but most of them are limited to specialties—ornithology, chemistry, photography, botany, and the like. Although almost wholly extracurricular, they are vital factors in American education and indirectly significant in community life. More than ten thousand such clubs are now affiliated with Science Clubs of America, which is an important activity of Science Service in Washington. The annual science talent search of the Science Clubs of America has pioneered the way to the program for national scholarships in the recently proposed legislation for a National Science Foundation.

The central organization assists the individual clubs through suggesting local activity programs, through encouraging regional cooperation such as annual science fairs, and through supplying information on cost-free or inexpensive materials for scientific studies or even research on a modest scale. Although but a few years old, the Science Clubs of America are becoming recognized as a significant activity of the country. For example, the national Weather Bureau cooperates with the Science Clubs through supplying rain gauges and instructions to groups. A large program involving experiments on growth is under consideration in connection with the educational work of the American Cancer Society.

The boys and girls in the Science Clubs of America will be the dominant citizens in a scientific age a generation hence. Their spirit, activity, and training at this time is a national concern. The hopes for the Science Clubs of America are fourfold and to me immensely important:

1. The central organization should have much increased resources in order that it can better serve the Science Clubs and promote the highly stimulating regional or state science fairs.

2. The Science Club movement should develop more widely as an important adult activity, of special importance in industrial areas where the present social development is moving in the direction of short hours and the mass production of leisure time.

3. The success of the local Science Clubs and of the national organization should encourage the formation and development of similar non-scientific organizations, in order that our culture be not distorted through the attraction of the alert and eager youth too preferentially into science. The analogue of science fairs would be arts and crafts exhibits, regional or statewide, for secondary school participants.

4. The Science Club movement should become international as soon as possible, and through our central organization we should arrange for international pairing of Science Clubs. For example, the Science Club of Princeton High School might be paired in a corresponding and collaborating way with the School Science Club of Melbourne, an earth's diameter away. There is no time to elaborate the potentialities of such an international movement among the

youth of the world. Already we have made preliminary steps, but the experience in America with the use and hopes of science societies, at this level, must first be presented and developed abroad.

There are nearly a thousand successful scientific and technological societies in America. The mortality is not high. Most of these societies will survive as long as American civilization lasts. A few will disappear through mergers, but many more will appear through budding and fission. At this professional level of scientific association, there is less sociability and more technical collaboration.

The American Astronomical Society is typical. Its membership of six hundred contains practically every astronomer and near astronomer and once-was-astronomer in the country, and annually it worries how far it should go for its members into the ranks of the amateurs and astrophiles. Membership is a recognition but not an honor. The future hopes of such societies, I would say, are (1) to keep the standards high in astronomical teaching and astronomical research; (2) to seek out and utilize vigorously the fruitful contacts between astronomy and other sciences; (3) to maintain without slacking the long-standing astronomical tradition that the stars are international, that the science knows no national boundaries, that world-wide cooperation is the essence of man's struggle against ignorance of the space-time complex and its energies.

Comparable descriptions and similar hopes could be expressed for the hundreds of societies in the physical and biological sciences, in the scientific professions and technologies.

The local interscience societies have a peculiar function to perform. It is the struggle toward the unity of science in an epoch of disunity that naturally arises from increasing specialization. The day of the encyclopedic mind has gone; it existed centuries ago only because the horizons were near.

We now attain some degree of encyclopedism through group action, but even so the comprehensive grasp and viewpoint are generally limited to a narrow strip through the increasing acreage of scientific knowledge. In a few of our universities in America and abroad, the searching minds gather informally and sporadically together, sometimes periodically, to see what gain may come from the widened attack on unknowns or uncertainties. These attempts to make deep and wide analysis by diverse experts should of course be much proliferated. Practical good can result. The funny questions a competent economist might ask about the orbit of Neptune, or about the nervous system of the giant squid, are far from valueless to the receptive celestial mechanic or the alert squidist.

Together with some associates I have of late contemplated the value of attempting to get a better insight through the deliberations of a small association of competent gropers from many disciplines into some of the basic problems of social policy, with the aim of formulating, where it seems possible, series of recommendations for the education and perhaps for the practical use of national policy makers. We can at least try, in these times of national and international confusion (and what times are otherwise?), to look calmly, deeply, and profitably into the problem, let us say, of the Negro in North America, examining it from the simultaneous standpoints of the anthropologist, philosopher, medical man, biochemist, climatologist, statistician, clergyman, lawyer, economist, historian, artist, as well as the sociologist and political scientist. Even from less relevant fields, like physics and mathematics, well-trained thinkers could usefully adjudicate evidence and argument.

Indeed the large problems of social policy, in community, state, nation, and for the total planet, merit serious attention by all specially trained citizens. The plan of operating

Social Policy Seminars among the faculties of aggressive universities must not be lightly dismissed. For these are tremulous days, and a phase of civilization is at stake.

The interscience organization that already exists, and which I would propose as an example of interscience activity, is the Society of the Sigma Xi, which now has the alternate name of The Scientific Research Society of America. With its one hundred forty chapters and clubs scattered throughout the institutions of higher learning and research in every state of the Union, and a total membership of approximately fifty thousand, Sigma Xi recognizes honorably through its election the creative ability of scientists, and through the activities of the local and national organizations performs numerous services that help to emphasize the interdependence of the sciences. The local chapters are of much importance and effectiveness in many institutions and of less significance in others, either because of indifferent personnel of the chapter and the dim spirit of the parent institution, or because the interscience problems are also the concern of other active local organizations.

The national organization of Sigma Xi chapters has grown much in usefulness in the past few years. Its quarterly, *The American Scientist*, is outstanding among scientific journals. Its national traveling lectureships, which now bring a total of about one hundred visits each year by recognized scientific experts to the Sigma Xi chapters and clubs, are an important service to the smaller or more isolated colleges and universities. The national society's research funds have helped many a scientist during the past two decades.

My hope for Sigma Xi, and for other societies that bring together the personnel and problems from all fields, is again that high standards be maintained, and that the responsibility of an election to the society will be placed far above the honor thereof. Additionally I hope that the traveling lecture plan can be gradually extended abroad, so that the international as well as the interscientific spirit of this society can be completely demonstrated.

But for the immediate future, a high-priority hope for the chapters and clubs of Sigma Xi is that they take an active part in the encouragement of scientific research in their respective institutions. Where active research committees are not already in existence, the local personnel of the Sigma Xi chapters should be of special service to the institution's administration through advice on all matters pertaining to the overall scientific programs. The establishment of progressive policies for state and nation in the training of scientists and support of scientific research, such as envisaged in the proposed National Science Foundation, is an activity in which the Sigma Xi can and should take conscientious part.

The international professional societies, such as the International Astronomical Union, and similar organizations in physiology and geophysics, are the somewhat loosely managed analogues of the national professional societies. They are numerous, because in science and technology an international attitude is easily accepted and is demonstrably possible. The hope for the future of these specialized worldwide societies is that they will grow in number and effectiveness, and so comport themselves that they will become clear demonstrations that international cooperation is neither difficult nor dangerous. If prime ministers could agree and cooperate on planetary problems in the way that astronomers agree and collaborate on galaxy-sized puzzles, the present world worries would be swiftly ameliorated.

In some respects the maximum of scientific organizations is attained in the science division of Unesco. Therein lies a possibility of great social profit, for this association of scientists and scientific bodies is truly international and truly interscientific. Concerning its uses up to now, I can say very little, for the organization scarcely exists. Concerning my hopes for it, the day is too short for even a summary.

The International Council of Scientific Unions is a small steering body that is both international and loosely interscientific; but it covers only a fragment of the general scientific field.

The United Nations Educational, Scientific, and Cultural Organization (Unesco) is as comprehensive as life itself. Its science division will be entrusted with activities that should lead toward the One-World idea. It recognizes the needs of thoroughly exchanging scientific literature and personnel throughout all nations of the world, of helping with bibliographies and summaries and abstracts, of assisting in the educational problems of some of the United Nations members that request assistance, and of handling in various ways all the scientific, educational, and cultural programs that may be referred to it by the United Nations. There will be money to do these things—perhaps many millions of dollars a year. There will be misunderstandings and confusions, of course, as well as noble services. We who watch it work must be constructive with criticism, cooperative with suggestions, patient, and tolerant. International good will is not a natural inheritance from the jungle, and we are having some difficulty in anchoring firmly in our characters this new and only partially acquired characteristic.

The primary and very appropriate hope for Unesco and its scientific division is that it shall not become sterile and futile. The issues are too big to be satisfied with routine bureaucracy. The possibility of cooperating internationally in scientific fields should be dramatically emphasized in the hope that the internationalism of science may lead to belief in the internationalism of human friendship.

I have been encouraged to make some suggestions about both the routine and creative activities of Unesco. My position as president of the American Association for International Education (which has worked especially on the project of getting enabling legislation passed by the American Congress), and my activity as a delegate from our State Department to the London conference, where Unesco's charter was written and as an adviser to the State Department on Unesco's work in science, has perhaps made it appropriate for me to urge enterprises of two types.

The first is the foundation of great international institutions for scientific exploration and development in fields where researches are normally so expensive that small institutions or even small countries cannot easily undertake them on a national basis. For instance, large and expensive telescopes could provide in an international observatory the suitable equipment for the investigations of astronomers from a score or more of countries where the equipment is now deficient. The exploration of the gaseous envelope is a world-wide, expensive, major operation, and in a peaceful world should not be nationally limited. Large scientifically equipped ships for the study of the life of the sea and the shores are expensive to build and maintain, as are large projects in human ecology, or for the development and exploitation of new food plants, or for a mass attack on some of man's major maladies—all such projects could, if the spirit were right, be handled better on the international rather than on the national basis. Therefore I propose serious consideration by Unesco of creating an international observatory, an international institute for the study of the gaseous envelope (ionosphere, meteorology, atmospheric physics, radio transmission, sun-earth relationships), a central institution with substations for the international exploitation of food plants; an international institution for the study of health and nutrition; an international marine biological station (perhaps located at Naples); and eventually an international center for the study, with great atom-smashing and transforming apparatus, of the nucleus of the atom.

The second enterprise that I have formally called to the attention of the Secretariat of Unesco is the establishment and operation of Unesco Traveling Panels, each composed of specialists of different nationalities and adjacent fields of specialization. For example, a recognized authority in each of the fields of nuclear physics, astronomy, geology, paleontology, and biology would constitute a world-wide traveling panel. I visualize these small groups of international experts traveling together from one cultural center to another throughout a whole continent with pauses of a week in each place for professional and public contacts. In my plan these traveling proponents of education, good will, and a higher civilization, would be men and women of high distinction, and their visits to the educational centers of the smaller countries would be an occasion for the general celebration not only of the unity and good-will message of the sciences, but also a living reminder of the oneness of all mankind.

DISCUSSION

UREY: I think it safe to say that we are probably more interested in Shapley's international suggestions than in some of his other remarks, because national activities of various kinds are pretty well established.

This session offers a suitable time for bringing out our present worries regarding the distribution of information. I refer to the problems of *secrecy*, which will face us in the future. I attended recently three scientific meetings; two of these were public and one was secret. The secret one was a meeting of the Manhattan Project; the two others were a meeting of the American Physical Society and a meeting of the American Chemical Society. If I were asked to rate them in order of descending interest from a purely scientific point of view, I would rate them as follows: first, the American Physical Society; second, the secret meeting; third, the American Chemical Society. (You must realize that the Chemical Society is likely to come last in any such ordering because its field consists so much of industrial applications rather than pure or basic research.) We can expect that in the future a part, at least, of our scientific research is going to be declared "classified." [1] Someone, somewhere—either scientists or government authorities—is going to declare part of our scientific activities to be secret, and this part will not be available for our scientific societies except if the latter are of a secret variety. I wish to suggest that this will result in a drift among scientists in one direction or the other, toward that which is public information or toward that which is

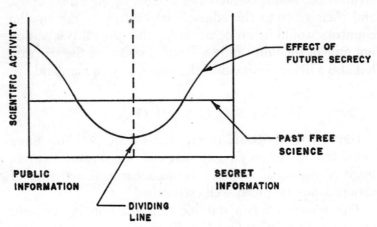

Figure 1. Urey's diagram

secret, and that there is likely to be a valley in the curve of scientific activity at the borderline subjects between those that are declared free and those that are declared secret. There is one solution to this problem of the borderline cases.

[1] In wartime nomenclature, *classified* information is secret except to certain people, *declassified* information is open to the public.

It is an improbable solution, but I believe it to be the only one which will restore uniform distribution of scientific activity. This solution is *international security*; and although the possibility of this solution is remote, I feel that there is no other. I cannot be sure that it is necessarily true that .problems of this kind do have a solution; probably the only thing that we can do is to struggle with the problem for some time to come.

ALLISON: I was frankly dismayed by Shapley's remarks, and I just wonder if he wasn't making them in a sense of irony. The idea that international nuclear science *can* exist at this time would be funny if it weren't so tragic. Whether we like it or not, in the minds of too many Americans nuclear science is merely a part of the military strength of the country which develops it, and it is not going to be shared with other countries because they might use it against us. Recently the newspapers reported the following exchange of remarks between an after-dinner speaker on atomic energy and his questioner. The speaker was asked, "How can you justify not disseminating information about nuclear science when the withholding of this information is holding back the progress in our own country?" His answer—and it was wildly applauded at the time—was, "We won't risk helping others a great deal even if thereby we hinder ourselves slightly." This shows the attitude, I am afraid, of the majority of our citizens. In the presence of this situation it is just silly to talk about an international convention in nuclear science.

SHAPLEY: Of course I was trying to be ironical in my remarks about nuclear science. I was expecting an objection, and I was going to reply as follows. So far as I know, no government has stopped astronomers from talking about the super novae, nor have they been stopped from discussing the Indians' theory of the high temperature of the corona which involves atomic fission, so you see that there are some things left; but you are quite right, and it is true that many people consider nuclear science a military secret. But I foresee that with the advent of biological warfare, this same question of secrecy will invade the sciences of biology and medicine as well.

CONDON: I wonder if we should have an international congress on nuclear science from which Americans would be excluded!

VANVLECK: In the past there have been some excellent international conferences in mathematics and also in some fields of physics less publicized than the nuclear one.

Physics is so widespread a field, involving so much personnel, that it may be a good procedure to have meetings on certain specific aspects of it. As an example of a very useful congress of this type I may cite the last such conference before the war, namely, the Strassburg conference on magnetism held in May 1939, less than three or four months before the outbreak of hostilities. It was the same city of Strassburg which only a few months later was brought under German guns. Nevertheless, at the conference there was an atmosphere of peacefulness and peaceful cooperation. In view of the state of the world at that time, this was a remarkable example of international cooperation. I think that we should have more similar conferences. The Strassburg congress was organized by the Institute of Intellectual Cooperation of the League of Nations. I hope that similar meetings will be sponsored internationally in the future.

BRIDGMAN: I should like to ask of the members present how many would be willing to work in secrecy. We all worked in secrecy during the war emergency, and did so gladly; but I think that the proportion willing to do so as a regular thing will be very small.

BREIT: I think this is so. This attitude arises because secrecy and concealment are the antithesis of the search for truth; the reason that the military strongly support secrecy is, of course, that they are dealing really in applied physics.

DuBridge: I should like to come back to the question of an international congress on nuclear physics which was raised a few moments ago. I see no reason for considering such a project as not feasible. After all, this is essentially an international conference on nuclear physics. And although it may not be possible to speak in such a conference with all the freedom which we might like ideally to see, it seems nevertheless perfectly possible to have an international conference on nuclear physics at the present time.

Tolman: I will discuss the declassification program of the Manhattan District. We are trying to set up a reasonable declassification policy. We have carefully sifted and considered the whole field of the work of the Manhattan Project, with the conclusion that there are three classes of information coming out of this project.

In Class 1 is contained all nuclear physics that is not directly related to construction of an atomic bomb. If you look at reports of the miscellaneous technical societies, if you look at the output that is now declassified but not yet published, or is made available to the proper channels of commerce, you will find an enormous amount of material. This material includes a good deal of industrial know-how which did not have anything to do directly with bomb manufacture.

In Class 2 we put scientific materials—pure science—which you would like to have declassified but which should not be. It is not industrial know-how so much as pure science which happens to be directly connected with bomb manufacture. It is thought for the time being that this should not be declassified; it is recommended that it should be kept in mind for declassification as soon as conditions warrant.

In Class 3 we put industrial know-how directly connected with bomb manufacture, and I am sure that its declassification would be of no great help to pure science.

I think that the declassification plan (which was set up by a committee consisting of Bacher, Arthur Compton, Oppenheimer, Urey, and Tolman, who was chairman) was a very successful scheme. The whole subject is a very complicated one to arrange. Certain divisions have to be dropped, countless problems have to be solved, new things have to be added, and the feeling of responsibility that you have for recommending modifications in the declassification guide makes the task a big one. I think that nuclear science is not being declassified as rapidly and as wisely as might be desired; but I'm sure that we now have enough declassified material to allow us to have a congress on nuclear physics.

WIGNER: Urey has emphasized the very serious possibility of science being divided into two categories. Thus, nuclear physics would be divided into two parts, depending on classification. One part would be common knowledge and one part not common knowledge. Such a split is certainly not a condition to look forward to. But we should not paint the future too dark either. I feel that the Manhattan District authorities are going to do better on the secrecy question than we feared they might. Another reason for my feeling that we need not worry so much about secrecy as we did at one time is that the atomic energy legislation has turned out so much better than we feared it would.

TOLMAN: I don't think that universities ought to work on science that is secret. It is completely out of keeping with the spirit of a university to work on anything that is secret; and I think the universities do wrong when they take money —and you can get a lot of money that way—to work on something that is secret. Now personally I only want to work on old-fashioned things like thermodynamics and there is nothing secret about them, and so this problem doesn't arise with me; but I know it is a very serious problem for a lot of universities. There is a lot of easy money floating around now that you can get if you work on something for the Navy or the Army. We ought to be very cautious about that sort of thing, and I think the only way to avoid it is to work on things that aren't secret.

UREY: I might say that in bringing up this subject I was not thinking of the Manhattan District only. I was speaking of a general trend that is likely to develop in the near future, arising from the general feeling of insecurity. It may extend to biology; it may extend to all sorts of fields. The general problem, not any specific one, is at the root of our difficulties with the Manhattan District.

BREIT: The problem of declassification is a many-sided one. One group concerned with it is the military, who do not know too much about the technical side of the question and who are very much concerned with the question of security; and considering the differences in the point of view of the military and scientists, I think that all in all a very admirable job has been done for which the people involved should receive the greatest credit.

FEYNMAN: The statement has been made that what was on the secret side is gadgetry, technical know-how, a kind of industrial secrecy. We're used to that. We've seen that before. Industries have kept their own little techniques of making ceramics that don't break down at too high a temperature, don't dissolve and so on. I think there really is a danger that not all the secret information is of that kind. Some of that which we used to regard as fundamental science is secret too. Thus, some of the fundamental nuclear constants are still on the secret side of the fence, and this presents a problem. It is not an immediate problem, since there is not much fundamental knowledge about the fission process. On the other hand we are only at the beginning, and once you start the practice of putting scientific knowledge under secrecy, it is likely to spread.

Here we are overlooking something which we preach and continue to preach to the military men all the time: "There isn't any secret science. Science is very easy. It's a universal subject. There are the same atoms all over the world. The Martians would obtain the same value for the number of neutrons liberated in fission that we would." Maybe the answer is that we should as soon as possible get all our friends in the other countries to measure all the quantities which are now on the secret side and publish them as rapidly as possible and point out that there are no fundamental secrets. Maybe that will teach the public the lesson that their only secrets are their technological ones. And so I am inclined to ask those in this room who are from other countries please to measure these things and publish them— please do so! It isn't very hard!

H. S. TAYLOR: Urey drew a graph which indicated that he expects scientific activity in the non-secret field to be of the

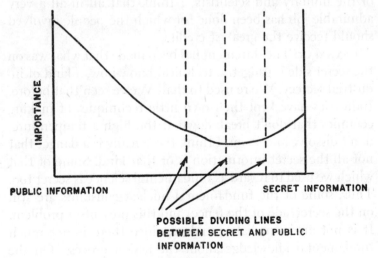

Figure 2. H. S. Taylor's diagram

same order of magnitude as scientific activity in the secret field. I suggest that if we consider *importance* rather than *quantity* of work, the balance would swing sharply to the side of the non-secret field. This is because the important things become secret only after their importance is discovered, and there isn't enough intelligence in military minds or many other minds to recognize the important things the moment they are discovered.

DuBridge: I am no defender of the military, but it seems to me that they deserve some defense. It isn't the military mind determining what is secret and what is not; it is the international situation. We are faced with a grave international situation; and as long as it exists even civilians, when faced with the responsibility of determining what should be secret and what should not be, will draw a line somewhere. The atomic energy declassification committee was a committee of civilians and the military adopted their recommendations. Let's not say that the military mind is at fault in this. As soon as we can get something that looks like secure world peace, these problems will vanish; and until they do vanish I think all civilians will have the same point of view whenever they are faced with the actual responsibility of making decisions.

Fermi: In this question of declassification there is a remarkable unanimity among people who know the technological importance of the information. I don't remember finding any essential disagreements about the philosophy; I found disagreements on the interpretation of the philosophy, but not very essential ones. I don't believe there are many who would advocate a widespread publication of technological know-how at this moment. As to basic scientific information, I think that most people in responsible positions agree that perhaps some seventy or eighty per cent of the scientific information gathered by the Manhattan District should be declassified and the remainder should for the time being, at least, be kept somewhat quiet.

There is, however, one point on which all of us who have been connected with the work are to some extent responsible. We have not made sufficient effort to write and publish this seventy or eighty per cent that could be published. This is partly due to laziness, and partly also to the difficulties involved in making sure that due credit is given to anyone who contributed to the work. But the present situation would improve if we all felt that we have a duty to do our best in order to publish promptly what can be published now.

HARNWELL: There is an unfortunate dilemma which has not been clarified here; and this is the following. If we have a moral obligation to keep certain areas of pure science secret, how is a person who does not know what these secret facts are to know how to direct his own research program? There may be, as DuBridge said, certain regions which should not be openly investigated. But if we do not know what they are, how are we to know what not to investigate? In other words, is a physicist likely to be considered disloyal because of pursuing an undirected experimental research program in nuclear physics?

TOLMAN: I think that if a physicist is working in his own laboratory not connected with the Manhattan District, is not spending government money, but is spending his own funds or money from his university, he ought to do any kind of research he wants to; and if he gets any interesting results I think he has a perfect right to publish them. But I also think that if he sees that his results have some immediate military application, he will probably wish to consult with imformed people as to whether it is wise for him to publish or is wiser to turn that research over to some secret government laboratory.

HARNWELL: I don't think the universities want to do secret research; but my question is, how do I know what to publish?

TOLMAN: Have you found out something that you think is secret?

HARNWELL: No, but I can imagine that I might find out

something. Should I then come to someone and say, "Can I publish this?" or should I say to myself, "I have found it out so I should publish it anyway." How am I to know?

TOLMAN: I think that when an actual specific question arises, you will have no doubt what to do. If it is something which seems to be pure science, go ahead and publish. If it seems to have any immediate military application, you will want to talk with the Atomic Energy Commission.

TURNER: One other point should be mentioned. The existence of this body of scientific information which is being kept secret is going to have a considerable indirect influence. No one is interested in devoting his time and his resources to working something out if he has the suspicion that it has all been done and is being hidden, and that successful results of his own would be suppressed. You may not be so annoyed that you turn to the study of the colors of butterfly wings, as someone once suggested; but at least you will shy away from the problematical areas of physics, because there is a lot of physics to be done, and you can easily find some field of study about the classification of which there can be no doubt. It seems to me that this is going to be of some importance in nuclear physics as long as there is a considerable body of pure scientific knowledge all worked out but withheld.

MAYER: There exists a law, in the McMahon bill, which most scientists have at least tacitly approved; and that bill in a way supersedes the Tolman declassification committee. In that bill, as I understand it, everything is secret unless it is specifically excluded. I am the editor of a scientific journal, and on reading the bill I find it impossible to decide as an editor whether I can accept any article on nuclear physics of any sort, even if it comes from abroad, without first submitting it to some competent authority to decide whether it should be declassified. I believe that the lawyers of the American Institute of Physics, in reading the bill, came to the conclusion that all editors, even if they should receive an article submitted from abroad, must submit it first to some authority set up by the commission in order to decide whether it can be published. The commission may be very liberal, but it appears that they have to sift everything non-secret; it is not that they make anything specifically secret, it is that everything is a priori secret until they decide it can be published. I hope that I am mistaken in that reading of the bill.

TOLMAN: You are quite correct. The McMahon bill, for which the scientists of America had such great hopes after hearings of about nine months, is, as far as concerns security, an atrocious bill. It got its worst characteristics right in the very last days, during the conference between the House and the Senate when they were trying to patch up contradictory notions which the Senators and the Representatives had. As a matter of fact, you can characterize Section Five of the bill by saying that the law "encourages and prohibits" dissemination of information. It is really extremely bad. For the purposes of governmental work you have to get a special letter from the President to tell you how things can be interpreted in the interim before the commission is set up. The commission has not yet been set up. I hope that when it is, it will have a sensible and liberal policy.

MORRISON: Just as an indication of the kind of difficulties that may arise, I think that certain paradoxes have already occurred in the Manhattan District with regard to this question, in the relation of British and American scientists working on the Manhattan project. I think it is probably no secret to say that since August 1, 1946, it has been the rule that where American and British scientists were working together, we were permitted to discuss with our colleagues only those things which were already known up to August 1, but nothing discovered thereafter. This was simply based upon the interpretation of the bill. A second and more serious difficulty occurred in the project at Los Alamos, with a man who is actually employed in the project and who was an applicant for American citizenship. Because he had not yet been naturalized and there was some thought that he might perhaps be shifted to some other laboratory, it was held that with him also no communication of new information was allowed. This made his position in the laboratory somewhat difficult!

RUSSELL: If there is to be any secrecy at all in these matters it can be justified only on the basis of public danger. If there is going to be secrecy on this account there has got to be some criterion. I think we all agree that the existing machinery for the criteria is pretty bad but I judge that there is hope that this commission may improve it. It seems to me though, that if we are going to have anything at all, the best we can do is to have some organization which can inform anyone in case of doubt where the limitations are, for each one of us to have a feeling of individual responsibility. I don't mean responsibility under the law of penalties, but moral responsibility—moral responsibility to make sure that one does not inadvertently trespass. The inadvertence might be completely honest, the trespass utterly disastrous. I feel therefore that we must have some machinery by which anyone in case of doubt may raise the question and have at least a quick answer, and in addition we must develop a sense of moral responsibility which will make us careful to refer questions to this body.

CONDON: The kind of body which Russell suggests will be provided by the Atomic Energy Commission when it has been set up. We are in a difficult interim period, and since at present there is no commission, I think that we should have a sort of informal organization such as that which Russell suggests, which could easily incorporate the policies of declassification. Of course we are still faced with the possibility that a person may not know the full implication of what he has discovered; but if he has reason to believe that what he has discovered involves the security of the United States, then he should take it up with the commission. Then if the commission tells him that there is no reason to believe that any question of security is involved, he is reasonably safe; and I think the restriction on publications wouldn't be as serious as we might fear.

MAYER: It seems to me that the interpretation of this commission's duties, as specified in the bill, means that anything new is automatically secret unless the commission specifically says that it is not. That seems to me to be a peculiarly unfortunate situation and is a much worse feature of the bill than any question of the size of penalties. It is not so much that the commission is empowered to determine what shall be secret, as that anything new is automatically secret until the commission declares otherwise.

CONDON: As one who worked for the government for several months and went through at least one hundred and fifty drafts of that particular section of the bill, I want to make one more comment. It is quite possible that there will be new material not yet known, which in the national interest it will be desirable to keep secret. You can't specify in advance what it is, and even afterward you will not be able to specify it, because that would be telling the secret. Nobody as far as I know was able to come up with a solution to the problem. I don't know any way out other than that of simply putting it in the hands of sensible people.

MAYER: I think that this situation ought to be publicized. There are bound to be things that the commission doesn't know of; but in spite of this, anything new which is found out is secret first, non-secret only after the commission has declassified it.

CONDON: You are right; that is a correct statement.

RUSSELL: The issue is fairly clear: if a new discovery is made, neither the discoverer before he makes the discovery nor the commission nor anyone else can know it previously; and the question is, who shall have the responsibility of deciding whether it should fall within the secrecy limits—the discoverer who knows nothing else and does not know the other things which are secret and their relation to one another, or the commission which does know these things? It seems to me that the answer is inevitably in favor of the latter.

THE PHYSICAL SCIENCES,
PHILOSOPHY, AND HUMAN VALUES

F. S. C. NORTHROP

THE issue that arises in this symposium as a whole is whether there is going to be any future for nuclear science—whether or not the release of atomic energy may not, because of the uses to which it is turned, lead to the destruction of science and civilization alike.

We had better begin as best we can by trying to translate these words "human values" and "philosophy" into some kind of more technical terminology and to put some content into them. One of the first mistakes commonly made in talking about human values is to assume that we know what they are. Nothing, it seems to me, is more obvious than that this thesis is false. Quite apart from the release of atomic energy and the resulting dangers is the fact of the ideological conflicts of our world. These are far more dangerous than the atomic bomb. If the atomic bomb is ever used to destroy civilization, it will be because men cannot get together sufficiently upon their ideologies to agree upon the social controls that are necessary to meet the situation. This is the fundamental issue confronting the world at the present moment: whether the ideology of the traditional French and Anglo-American democracies and that of Russian communism are so incompatible that we simply cannot get together, whether we mistrust each other's aims and thus cannot find any basis for discussion of the issues that confront us politically.

Heaven knows the issues are difficult enough—selfish nationalistic pride, the drive for oil and natural resources all over the world. Science intensifies these competitive factors because the nations with scientific knowledge must drive for resources to feed their machines, and these drives are hard enough to control even when the situation is not aggravated by ideological conflicts having their sources in the humanities.

It is important to make an analysis of these ideological conflicts and get out into the open the assumptions that underlie them. Let us take as two examples the doctrine of Russian communism and the ideology underlying the classical Anglo-American democracies. The humanistic theory of the ends of human activity in any specific ideology is not clear until one specifies its technical economic doctrine, its specific political doctrine, and its precise religious doctrine if it happens to have one. Most doctrine in any subject is not properly understood until its fundamental basic assumptions are exhibited. In any doctrine, whether it be a theory in natural science or an ideological theory in the humanities, there are certain basic assumptions.

Consider first the classical Anglo-American theory. Were one to ask a classical humanist in the United States what kind of society he would set up as the good end at which to aim, he would probably specify the type of society, so far as economics determines that society, which is defined by the classical economic theory that arose in Great Britain with Adam Smith and came to its final form in the economic science of Jevons. In this theory the basic entities are goods associated with pleasure. Jevons tells us frankly at the beginning of his *Principles of Political Economy* that the basic thing governing all economic actions is the quest for pleasure and freedom from pain. Certain economic wants of men have associations of pleasure, others have associations of pain, some have associations of a greater amount of pleasure than do others, and it is this greater amount which increases wants for them. The total number of wants as added up in the market place determines the demand, and scarcity due to the limitations of nature determines the supply. The law of supply and demand and the theory of prices generally come out of the relationship between these two factors.

Jevons is perfectly explicit in saying that the person who justifies these assumptions is the *philosopher* Bentham. Thus Jevons's economic theory presupposes a specific philosophical theory.

Similarly, the political theory of the good society in the traditional United States—the one that went into its Declaration of Independence and into its Constitution—is rooted in a specific philosophy. Professor J. P. Miller in his *Origins of the American Revolution* makes it perfectly clear that the whole community mind at that time was literally steeped in the philosophy of John Locke. Professor Miller writes that Locke functioned in determining the "idea of the good" that went into the Declaration of Independence and the Constitution in precisely the same manner that Marx functioned in determining the ideological assumptions of the Russian Communistic Revolution of 1918. Thus the classical Anglo-American social ideology in both its economic and its political content is rooted in and presupposes for its justification the philosophical assumptions of modern British empirical philosophy.

This British empirical philosophy and in particular the philosophy of Locke was determined in considerable part by Galilean and Newtonian physics, as this physics was first understood and described by Galilei and Newton themselves. The Lockean philosophical theory is that the whole of the universe—both nature and man—is to be understood as an aggregate of physical objects, termed by Locke and Descartes "material substances," which are located in public mathematical space and which act upon observers who project back colors and sounds in sensed space and time as appearances. This distinction between sensed qualities in private relative sensed space and time and physical objects or material substances in public mathematical space and time is put quite clearly by Newton in the "Scholium" at the beginning of his *Principia.* There Newton points out that the sensed space and time in which sense qualities are located must never be confused with the public mathematical space and time within which the public objects of physics are situated.

Immediately the question arose, not merely for physicists but also for all modern philosophers, concerning what the relation is between the relative sensed space and time, with its sense qualities which we directly observe, and the public mathematical space and time, within which the public objects of physics are located. The answering of this question was the basic task bequeathed to early modern philosophy by Galilean and Newtonian physics.

The answer was specified for Locke and other early modern philosophers by Galilei and Newton themselves. Both Galilei and Newton assert that the sense qualities in relative private sensed space and time which we directly observe are the way in which the public material objects in public mathematical space and time *appear* to the observer. Put more precisely, this means that sense qualities in sensed space and time are related to physical masses in public mathematical space and time by a three-termed relation in which the sense qualities in sensed space and time are one term; the physical objects, or material substances, in public mathematical space and time are a second term; and the observer is the intermediary, third term. Without the observer, there would be no sensed qualities and no relative private sensed space and time.

All the latter sensuous factors are mere projections from the observer. This is what Newton meant when he called them "appearances."

Physical objects in public mathematical space exist, however, even when no one is looking and no observers are

VICTORIA COLLEGE
No.
LIBRARY

present. This is what Newton meant by calling them "real." To say, moreover, as Newton did, that the sense data in sensed space and time are appearances of the public physical masses in public mathematical space and time is to add a further qualification with respect to the role of the observer in the relationship between the two, the qualification, namely, that the observer does not project the sense qualities in sensed space and time spontaneously, but only does so when he is acted upon by the material substances in public mathematical space and time. Note, however, that this is precisely the philosophy of man and nature of John Locke, the philosophy which asserts that the whole of reality is to be conceived as material substances in public space, acting upon observers who project back sense qualities in private sensed space and time as appearances.

To sense the full philosophical consequences of Galilei's and Newton's physics as made explicit in Locke's philosophy, it is necessary, however, to note what is entailed concerning the nature of the observer. The observer cannot be conceived as merely an aggregate of the material substances of his body, since the latter type of observer would be quite unable to be conscious of sense qualities in sensed space and time as appearances. This follows as both Galilei and Newton emphasized, because material substances have only the properties of moving in a straight line with a constant velocity when no external forces are acting upon them and of moving in an accelerated manner when acted upon by external forces. Material substances, furthermore, have no consciousness and hence no capacity to be aware of ineffable sensuous qualities in sensed space and time as appearances. Thus Locke saw that the Galilean and Newtonian observer had to be a different kind of substance from the material substances or even the aggregate of material substances in mathematical space and time. This unique type of substance Locke called a "mental substance." Thus, put more precisely, the Lockean mental substance is simply the kind of entity identified with the observer which has the property such that, when it is acted upon by the material substances of physics in mathematical space and time, it has the consciousness of, and the capacity to project back, sense qualities in sensed space and time as appearances.

The point which led us into all these scientific and philosophical distinctions and technicalities has now been demonstrated. This point was that the Lockean philosophy which defined the economic and political ideology of classical Anglo-American culture was not merely a philosophy of economic science and politics but also the philosophy to which Galilean and Newtonian physics first forced modern philosophical thought. Since Lockean philosophy was a necessary consequence of distinctions drawn by Galilei and Newton themselves in the Newtonian physics which was experimentally verified, it followed for Locke and his followers that the Lockean philosophy was not merely an idea of the good for the state and for culture but also a philosophy of the experimentally verified for nature.

Locke had no alternative, therefore, but to identify the human soul or personality in religious discussion and the political person in legal theory and the state with the person as conceived by his philosophy, that is, with the mental substance which functions as the intermediary second term in the three-termed relation joining apparent sensed qualities in apparent sensed space and time to the physical objects in mathematical space and time.

In this Lockean theory of the nature of the person, there are no imaginable relations whatever between one person or mental substance and another. Mental substances are not related spatially. This is what Leibnitz meant when he termed them "windowless monads." It is this lack of any intrinsic social relations between persons which is the Lockean modern foundation of the political philosophy expressed in the American Declaration of Independence to the effect that there is no basis for government, no normative social theory, apart from a social convention.

The significance of the latter point will be grasped if we compare the concept of the person of Galilean and Newtonian physics and the attendant Lockean philosophy with the concept of the person of Aristotelian physics and the attendant Thomistic philosophy or theological polity of the English Tudor Hooker. According to Aristotelian philosophy and science, personality is embodied soul, where soul is the form of the living body. Aristotle explicitly says in his psychology that the study of the soul falls within the science of nature. This soul or form of the living body is related organically to the forms or final causes of all other living creatures. Consequently, the concept of a person in the Aristotelian sense is one in which the individual person is part of a hierarchical order of species and genera defined by the scientific method of classification in science of the natural history descriptive type. This conception of a person as involving a position in a hierarchical order which relates his individual nature essentially to the individual natures of other persons and creatures throughout the cosmos is what Aristotle had in mind when he said that man is in his essential nature a "political animal." Man's individual nature is a social nature. He cannot be himself as an individual man except as he is part of a social organization or state which embodies the hierarchical relation of himself to all other creatures and natural objects. Thus in the Aristotelian theory of a person, a person is organically related to other people and must have this relation expressed in society if society is to give expression to his own individuality. Consequently a good state is one in which a man cannot be himself except in so far as he operates through an organized social church and through an organized political government. But in the Lockean theory, in which one cannot even imagine what the relation is between one person or mental substance and another, there are no scientifically and philosophically defined and grounded relations to be used in defining political theory. Consequently Lockean and classical Anglo-American modern political theory has no alternative but to ground government in nothing more than a convention, that is, in the consent of the governed.

The Marxian theory of a person and of politics is similarly opposed to the Lockean conception and much nearer to that of Aristotle, even though different also from the position of the Greek. According to Marx there is no meaning to the individual human nature apart from the organic structure of society which in turn cannot be conceived apart from a particular stage of the historical process. Furthermore, the key factors in the definition of an understanding of both human nature and any stage of the historical process are economic in character and economic in a materialistic, thermodynamically physiological sense.

All these considerations indicate that differences in ideology in the social sciences and the humanities are rooted in differences in the philosophies underlying these ideologies and that the philosophies in turn are connected with the results of scientific inquiry and are always regarded by the people who hold them as called for by the scientific knowledge which they take into account. Put more concretely, what this means is that any people are impressed by the facts of their experience which fall within their attention. From these facts they derive, consciously or unconsciously, a specific scientific generalization or theory. The analysis of this theory, after the manner in which Locke analyzed the physics of Galilei and Newton, brings out an explicit philosophy. In terms of this philosophy they define their economic, political, religious and other humanistic doctrines and attendant social institutions. The good state is the state which permits the person to be the kind of person which such a scientifically verified philosophy designates a person to be.

If this analysis be true, we would expect that when for any reason a given philosophy is changed, then the social humanistic ideology and values will also change. Many considerations indicate this to be the case. For example, in the Middle Ages human values underwent considerable change in the shift within Roman Catholicism from the definition of its theological doctrine in terms of the philosophy and science of Plato to the formulation in terms of that of Aristotle, a shift which came in the theology of St. Thomas Aquinas. In the transition from the medieval to the modern world a similar reconstruction of ideology took place with the shift from the philosophy of St. Thomas to that of Locke and then to that of Hume, Bentham, and Jevons. And even since then, in the movement beyond British empiricism, through Kant to Hegel and Marx, another shift in ideology has occurred, which exhibits itself in Germany and Russia.

Unless the latter shift is kept continuously in mind we will forget that practically every person east of the Rhine, either a Russian or a German, for at least the last one hundred and fifty years, takes it for granted that the pre-Kantian British empirical philosophy underlying the ideology of the traditional modern French, British, and American world is completely outmoded. The intellectual leaders in philosophy and the social sciences in both Germany and Russia since the time of Kant regard it as established that considerations in mathematical physics which Kant, among others, made evident have completely disposed of British empirical philosophy as an adequate theory of scientific knowledge or of political, economic and other humanistic institutions. What convinced Kant and those following him of the inadequacy of British empirical philosophy was mathematics and mathematical physics. It became evident to all competent students of these subjects that it is impossible to define the technical concepts of mathematics or the concept of causality as it is used in mathematical physics in terms of nothing but sense data and their sequences as the philosophy of Hume requires. The British empirical philosophy, also, gives one no correct theory whatever of historical cultural evolution, with the shift and negations between different ideologies noted in the previous paragraph, which the evidence of history unequivocally indicates to be the case.

It was noted at the outset that the problem of establishing proper social controls of the scientific instruments which the natural sciences and engineering are now placing at the disposal of men centers at bottom in the problem of resolving the ideological conflicts between the different conceptions of economic and political theory and human values of the different nations and peoples of the world. The foregoing analysis has now made it evident that these ideological conflicts center at bottom in philosophical differences and that the philosophical differences in turn are connected with scientific theory concerning nature and the methods of scientific verification in natural science. Any approach to the resolution of the ideological problems, therefore, must begin by getting out into the open the differing technical economic, political, and religious doctrines of the different ideologies and the basic differing philosophical premises from which the economic, political, and religious doctrines stem. In the case of classical German culture of the nineteenth century, these philosophical premises were the post-Kantian premises of the philosophy of Hegel. In the case of the contemporary communistic Russian ideology the philosophical premises are those of the post-Kantian and post-Hegelian philosophy of Marx. In the case of classical traditional Anglo-American political economic theory they are those of pre-Kantian modern British empirical philosophy.

There are many other ideological conflicts in the world.

When all these different ideologies and their underlying differing philosophies are brought out into the open, two possibilities are found to be present.[1] Two given ideologies may presuppose philosophies which, while different, are nonetheless compatible. This is the case with the ideologies of the traditional East and the traditional West. Certain other ideologies may not merely differ in their basic philosophical premises, but these premises may be contradictory. The pre-Kantian British empirical philosophy underlying the Anglo-American economic and political values and the Marxist post-Kantian and post-Hegelian philosophy underlying the ideology of contemporary Russia is an example of the second possibility.

In the former case, where the philosophies at the basis of the differing ideologies, while different, are nonetheless compatible, the reconciliation is easy, comparatively speaking. One needs merely to enlarge the philosophical assumptions and the different values of the one ideology to include those of the other.

The real difficulty arises in the case where the underlying philosophies are not merely different but mutually contradictory. In this instance the manner in which ideological reconciliation is to be achieved is by no means easy or obvious.

It should be clear, however, that one must get some criterion outside the social sciences and humanities which can serve as an objective check or measure of the correctness of one ideology as compared with another. What kind of a criterion is one to obtain? Is there any criterion for an ideology that is objective? Is there any basis for saying that a given ideology is verified for everybody, Russian communists and Anglo-Americans alike?

The answer to all these questions was given by Socrates

[1] See the author's *The Meeting of East and West*, Macmillan Company, 1946.

and Plato in the *Republic*. There they say that only those who have passed through the hypotheses of the mathematical physical sciences can arrive at the idea of the good which one has a right to say holds for everybody.

Is it not extraordinary that Socrates and Plato should inform us that if we want to arrive at an idea of the good in the humanities and the social sciences which holds for everybody we have to investigate the hypotheses and basic concepts of the natural sciences? Perhaps the best way to explain this is to consider the method of the philosophy of science as we noted it to be illustrated in the passage from the physics of Galilei and Newton to the philosophy of Locke.

In this and all other natural sciences there is the aggregate of empirical data from which eventually, as in the case of Newton, a deductively formulated theory is derived. Such a theory has specific postulates which are expressed in terms of basic primitive concepts. When such a deductive theory is verified by the empirical experimental methods of science, which give the same results for one person who pursues them with understanding as they give for another, we clearly have in such deductive theory a set of propositions which, if they are true or verified for one person are also verified or verifiable for any other person. Providing, therefore, that one can specify methods by which such verified, deductively formulated theory in the natural sciences is shown to entail a philosophy, one will then have verified philosophical theory. When this verified philosophical theory is used to define one's idea of the good for culture, one can say that this idea of the good for culture holds for everybody, since its basic foundation is a philosophy derived from verified scientific theory of nature in which the verification is of a character such that it is valid for everybody.

It remains, therefore, in order to derive our objective criterion for judging conflicting ideologies, to specify the method of the philosophy of science by means of which the philosophy of experimentally verified deductively formulated theory in natural science is made articulate. This method Plato and Socrates called "dialectic." Careful analysis shows that "dialectic" is nothing more than logical analysis.

This analytic method of the philosophy of science has two parts. One part consists in analyzing the deductively formulated empirically verified theory of natural science to determine the primitive concepts in its postulates. These concepts designate the elementary and hence ultimate entities and relations in terms of which nature and man as part of nature is at bottom to be conceived. Such a specification of ultimate entities and relations is precisely what one means by a philosophy. Such philosophy was called by the Greeks "ontological philosophy," since these elementary entities and relations designate that which the verified theory indicates nature to be. The second task of analysis in the philosophy of natural science consists in analyzing the method of verifying the deductively formulated theory in question, and noting the connection between the concepts of the theory and the observable data of experience. This part of the philosophy of science designates what the Greeks called "epistemological philosophy," which the scientifically verified theory exhibits and entails. An instance of this appeared in the distinction made by Galilei and Newton between sensed space and time and mathematical space and time. This is an epistemological distinction. Thus the Newtonian and Galilean physics, as thus described by Galilei and Newton themselves, clearly and unspeculatively entailed a specific epistemological philosophy.

When the ontological results of the analysis of one's scientific theory of nature and the epistemological results of the analysis are combined, one has a complete philosophy. The important thing to note is that the epistemological part

designates, as we indicated in the case of the relation between Newton and Locke, not merely a scientifically verified theory of nature but also a scientifically verified theory
of man as the observer or knower of nature. Thus out of the
philosophy of natural science one necessarily and automatically obtains, under analysis, a philosophy of human
nature also.

We arrive, therefore, at this very important conclusion,
first designated by Socrates and Plato, but still true, nonetheless, as our previous examination of Locke's relation to
Galilei and Newton have indicated: That philosophy of the
good for the social sciences and the humanities is a publicly valid one which is also the philosophy of the experimentally verified theory of the natural sciences.

In other words, in a properly constructed society the
philosophy which underlies the definition of one's economic
doctrine, one's political doctrine, one's religious, poetic and
artistic theory must be identical with the philosophy of the
natural sciences which is determined by nothing more than
the logical analysis of the experimentally verified theories
of the natural sciences to bring out their primitive ontological assumptions and their methodological and epistemological assumptions. The philosophy of the good in culture
and the humanities, which defines the ends of human action, must be identical with the philosophy of the scientifically verified theory of the natural sciences, which, when
pursued with respect to its deductive consequences, provides the instruments for human action. Such a philosophy
of the good or the ideal in the social sciences and the humanities may be truly said to be an ideology which holds
for everybody since, being at the same time entailed by the
experimentally verified, deductively formulated theory of
the natural sciences, it is thereby verified by the methods of
natural science, which give the same result for one person
that they give for another.

This is the thesis which I would like to suggest to you as the answer to the question concerning the proper relation between the natural sciences, philosophy and human values. One tragedy of our civilization is that whereas science has gone forward, the separation of the departments of knowledge has obscured the essential connection between ideological or humanistic philosophy and the philosophy of natural science. As a consequence, our ideological philosophies have not changed along with changes in our philosophy of the natural sciences. Thus we find ourselves with a set of ideas grounded often in outmoded philosophies or in partial philosophies which get into conflict with each other. Hence the conflict of moral and social ideologies.

The previous considerations do, however, suggest a technique by means of which these ideological conflicts can be resolved. The fact that the criterion derives from natural science means that it is one which should work in our relationship to the Russians. For the Russians, likewise, believe in scientific method and in the natural sciences. They, like us, believe in the values of scientific inquiry applied to the resources of nature to lift the well-being of men in general and applied to the understanding of the dialectical evolution of their social institutions to enlighten the minds of men socially.

There is little likelihood of the Russians and us getting together upon the basis of a purely humanistic philosophy, since in the more ideological humanistic sphere the doctrines unequivocally contradict one another. But there is a real possibility, because of the considerations just noted, of the Russians and the members of the traditional democracies west of the Rhine finding a philosophical basis for agreement, providing this basis is rooted in a philosophy of the natural sciences. It may be that in this manner we can resolve the ideological conflicts which at present prevent the leaders of the major nations of the world from agreeing upon the forms of international social control necessary to direct the technological discoveries of natural science to good rather than destructive ends.

DISCUSSION

CHANDRASEKHAR: It may be said quite generally that scientific values are attained in a larger or a smaller measure in extending, or equivalently, limiting the domain of validity of certain basic concepts and in this way helping to formulate concepts of wider scope and generality. In practice what a scientist tries to do is essentially to select a certain domain and see if it takes its appropriate place in a general scheme which has form and coherence. If it does not, then he seeks further information which will help him toward such a general scheme. The principle being stated in this way, it is clear that all aspects of science are worth pursuing and none should be neglected, and in any case no one should feel sorry for investigating aspects of science which may not appear fundamental at a given time.

All these are rather obvious remarks, and it would hardly be necessary to make them were it not for the danger that in our justifiable enthusiasm for the new field of nuclear physics we may ignore or discourage the development of those parts of physics which consist in deriving and extending the range of established concepts—such fields as chemical physics or the nonrelativistic quantum theory. Indeed, it appears that at the present time there is an increasing tendency towards a division and a lack of understanding between those who are pursuing fundamental physics and those who are pursuing what may be called derived physics. If this tendency is present, as I think it is, and if it should increase, as I think there are indications that it may, then we should be apprehensive. Earlier generations have not yielded to such a tendency. For example from the time of

Newton to the beginning of this century, the whole science of dynamics and its offshoot, celestial mechanics, have consisted almost entirely in the amplification, in the elaboration, and in the working-out of the consequences of the laws of Newton, Halley, Laplace, Lagrange, Hamilton, Jacobi, and Poincaré; all were content to spend a large part of their scientific efforts in establishing and enlarging on the laws of Newton, that is, in the furtherance of a *derived* science. A disparagement of the derived aspects of science, implying as it would a denial of those values which these men have so earnestly sought, is to my mind sufficiently absurd to merit no further consideration. Again during the nineteenth century when the foundations of the great laws of thermodynamics, of statistical mechanics, and of electromagnetic theory were being laid, developments which in their way are as fundamental as any that have taken place since, the minds and hearts of those involved in those developments were not overshadowed by them exclusively. We have only to glance through the collected papers of Kelvin, of Stokes, of Maxwell, or of Rayleigh to realize how many-sided and widespread were the interests of these men.

One can multiply such examples. But it must be apparent to an impartial observer that there is a complementary relation between the basic and the derived aspects of science. The basic concepts gain their validity in proportion to the extent of the domain of natural phenomena which can be analyzed in terms of them, and in limiting the domain of validity of these concepts we recognize the operation of other laws more general than those with which we have operated. Looked at in this way, science is a perpetual becoming; and it is in the sharing of its program, in common effort, that the values of science are achieved.

MARGENAU: The problem to which we are chiefly devoted is the relation between the natural and the normative sciences. According to Northrop the natural sciences should, on analysis of their contents and their procedure, largely determine the normative ones: in a sense, *fact* should determine *value*. My remarks are intended to draw attention to the kind of linkage that exists (or can be made to exist) between science and the humanities, and particularly between exact natural science and ethics.

Admittedly, unless science provides a rational basis for ethics, modern life is likely to decay. Nevertheless, science is not equipped with devices capable of rendering ethical judgments. While it may tell you how one may kill most efficiently, it will not—in my opinion, it will never—tell you whether it is right to kill. This limitation of science arises from a feature of its methodology, which I next consider.

There is an increasing recognition, among students of the exact sciences at least, of the fact that science never leads to a unique ontology. From this arise the present hostility to metaphysics and the present strength of the positivistic trend in physics and mathematics. I believe that no amount of scientific research conducted within the frame of its accepted procedures will expose the kind of being needed to produce the content of ethics and religion. There can thus be no continuity of structure between and no immediate passage from the field of natural science to that of so-called values. It is impossible to evolve the latter from the former in the manner of the scientific humanist.

But though the philosophy of science is non-committal with respect to *ontology*, it provides an immensely fruitful basis for *epistemology*; and it is through epistemology that the contact with the humanities can and must be made. Our discussions here, exhibiting as they did methodology in action at the point of intimate contact between science and the atomic unknown, have strengthened my conviction that it is the *method* rather than the *content* of science that forms the link between science and ethics.

In the exact sciences success follows upon the completion of three stages of work: first, postulation of general principles; second, logical or mathematical deduction of specific theorems from the postulates; last, the empirical verification of the specific predictions. The order of these three need not always be the same.

Ethics can be a science with the same threefold structure. Its postulates, different though they are from those of the sciences, are no more sacred and no less binding to the individual who accepts them than are the axioms of arithmetic. The implications of this view are many. Ethics can disclaim all essential connection with religion, though it may still rely on religion as a reinforcing agent. Also, the act of dedication of an individual to a set of ethical postulates may be psychologically very close to a religious experience. Immoral acts could be viewed as irrational and inconsistent, rather than as offenses against a divine or human order. The teaching of ethics would have to be completely overhauled.

The second stage of ethics would be the explication of the postulates into a specific moral code. The third and the most fascinating stage is posed by the question: how does, or how can, ethics verify its moral code? There is one striking instance; a set of ethical postulates may destroy a society which espouses it. Apart from this "singular" case, I believe it to be possible to envisage ways beyond the scope of this discussion in which the verification of an ethical code may be achieved.

If science is to affect the humanities, reliance must be placed upon its methodology. I fear that amalgamation will be prevented if an "analytic continuation" of the subject-matter of the sciences into the realm of the humanities is sought.

DARROW: I should like to pose a concrete question. Let us define a communist as a person who opposes private ownership of a farm or a factory, and a democrat as a person who favors private ownership. Does Northrop mean to say that if we physicists were to come to agreement among ourselves on the basic doctrines of theoretical physics, then either the communist would give up his opposition to private ownership or else the democrat become opposed to it?

NORTHROP: The solution I suggested does not depend only on getting one deductive theory in physics to take care of all data. We can get enough philosophy for present needs to handle this Russian-vs-Democratic situation. However, in epistemological philosophy an analysis tries to do better, leaving open what the basic things are. Nevertheless, I believe actually that the Marxian theory does rest on an ontological argument.

To look at the question of the relation of the person to society from a scientific viewpoint; a person is, first of all, a thermodynamic system. Further, he is a thermodynamic system which has not yet attained the state of maximum entropy. This means that he requires to take energy in from the outside world if he is to survive. If the foregoing is your conception of a person and if from it you derive your conception of the state, then you may not want to trust this energy-supply for all men to the workings of free enterprise. In fact, you will probably believe that the first requirement of a good state is that it shall set up a social organization on the assumption that people must have food to eat.

It is not wise to begin with a concrete question. First we should get an epistemological philosophy formulated and get the concept of the person, and then see what kind of society would give the best expression to that concept of the person.

DARROW: This way of expressing the situation seems to imply that the necessity for eating was not realized until after the second law of thermodynamics had been formulated.

H. S. TAYLOR: I think that Northrop's position is that he

is interested in being a philosopher and not in being an economist.

NORTHROP: I do think that the philosopher has that responsibility and is obliged to accept it. It leads him to formulate a contemporary philosophy. He needs to derive, from his current philosophy, his economic theory and then his political theory.

BLACKETT: I ask whether Northrop did not a little exaggerate the influence of Galileo, Newton, and Locke. I understood him to say that the revolution in morals and ethics was in a very close way derivative from changes in scientific theory due to Galileo and Newton. Now when one studies that period one finds, as one conspicuous element in the moral and ethical climate, the gradual change in the status of the idea of lending money for a fee—usury, it was formerly called. Usury was originally considered by the Catholic Church to be a sin; but it is perfectly clear that this doctrine was becoming outmoded by the growing economic expansion in the years from 1600 to 1700 even though the Catholic Church maintained its attitude. Eventually the doctrine that usury is a sin completely disappeared because of the rising social necessity for money-lending. This revolution in the course of 150 years completely interchanged the "good" and the "bad." It is certainly *not* true historically that this revolution in morals was derivative from Galileo and Newton. It began a long time before them. I should like to ask whether Northrop has not overestimated the effect of science and philosophy on morals.

NORTHROP: I think that the scientific revolution played a very great part, because if you get any change in basic assumptions your values will always change. But the reason I believe that historically this has played a very great part is that before you can get an ideology that can capture the people you have to get agreement on that ideology, and that has got to have some kind of persuasive power. The great discoveries of the opening-up of trade could also change economics.

BLACKETT: My point is that these scientific ideologies did not make their impact on the population of England until the end of the seventeenth century, and by that time the ethical revolution was already forty years over.

HAWKINS: In the spirit of Bohr's ideas, I should like to suggest that when viewing the past we are able to consider men as being both products of history and producers of history. When we view our own generation, we have the same two aspects but may in practice be able to alter their relative prominence. We have as practical human beings the problem of so altering our ideas that they correspond more closely to the actual world. Thus, in connection with the question about private ownership of property, I suggest that we should refer not only to the basis in physical science upon which our ideas of modern physics depend but also to the empirical basis of ideologies, to the social studies. The problem of private property will be seen in a different light if we realize not only that man must eat well in order to live well, but also that the institution of private property is already altered from that which is described in the ideology of Locke. Locke said that a man's property is that which he produces. In our own society the nature of property is no longer that; and this fact is very relevant to an understanding of the meaning of Lockean ideology today.

ROBERTSON: I believe that each natural scientist has a philosophy whether he will admit it or not, and those who do not explicitly recognize that they have such a philosophy are apt to go off the deep end, as recent history has shown. I want to speak briefly of one point concerning the relationship between the various "levels"—the Platonic-Socratic view of the relationship of various stages of induction and deduction. It is quite possible that we can come to some agreement on epistemology, at least in the subjects of physics and chemistry. But as yet, I think, we have not. I see no reason for entertaining hope of agreement on the deeper metaphysical level.

Scientists have varying epistemological views, particularly in quantum theory and relativity theory. Developments in natural science in the last twenty or thirty years have led them to think more about the nature of the knowledge which they have acquired. The solutions to which they have come are not irreconcilable, but the attitude which they take towards the status of this knowledge differs from one person to another. One can evaluate scientific methodology by starting from the positivistic operational viewpoint of Bridgman, which I think must be acceptable to all scientists as a neutral point of departure. But is it broad enough to include all aspects? This is a difficult question on which there is no unanimity.

Among professional physicists there is a variety of attitudes toward either the epistemological or the ontological problem. I mention first Eddington, who tries to show that a great many of the principles of natural science are epistemological in origin—they are not merely affected by epistemological considerations, they are epistemological laws. This is a definite view of the nature of physical laws, which fortunately we are not compelled to share. There is also the attitude of Milne, who wants to start from certain authoritarian principles forming a basis for a deductive system; this I think to be definitely counter to the trend of modern science.

To sum up: while I believe that we may perhaps arrive at some reasonable agreement regarding the description and nature of our scientific method, the deeper ontological problem presents a variety of solutions, and it is not necessarily true that scientists must eventually agree on one of them. In particular, we may be free to choose between accepting and rejecting metaphysics, and our choice may materially affect the relations between the natural sciences on the one hand, and the social sciences and the humanistic fields on the other.

MEES: In discussing the possibility of an ontological development based upon physical science, Northrop seems to have assumed that we already have the necessary data—that we know physical science as a whole. Yet there is one department of physical science of which at present we know absolutely nothing, and so long as we do not know it we cannot form a general analysis of physical theory leading to a basic philosophy. I refer to *the nature of life*. We have no physical idea of it at present, and until we do have such a one—some picture of the nature of life in terms of physical sciences—we are unable to form a philosophy of life. Man is not merely a physiological engine; he is a living soul; he is composed of living cells, as are all animals. We do not understand the difference between a living and a dead cell. We can define the difference in terms of the behavior of the cell, but we have no basic theory of it. Schrödinger made an attempt, a very interesting and beautiful attempt, in his recent little book, to discuss the problem. There he has put out a most daring and imaginative hypothesis of the basis of life, which few of us would accept. But until we really know the basis of life, we are in the position of physical science before Galileo and Newton did their work.

VALLARTA: I ask you to turn your eyes to the south, to the countries beyond the southern frontier of the United States. The Spanish colonies in America derived from the very definite Spanish tradition, which governed their development. Then, at the beginning of the nineteenth century, the impact of the French encyclopedists was felt, and particularly one form of French philosophy, namely the positivist philosophy of Comte. An attempt was made to organize such a Latin-American country as Mexico on the basis of that philosophical theory. All our fundamental laws, our constitution, our whole organization were based upon that philosophy. This state of affairs continued for considerably more than half a century. It was not until 1910 or thereabouts that this system fell, and again an attempt was made to organize the state on the basis of a philosophy of a different character. Thus to the south of this country, attempts have been made on a very large and practical scale to construct a whole society on such a basis.

VANVLECK: I'm rather sceptical about the impact of mathematics and physics on the man on the street. There are those of us who struggle with teaching physics and who realize the impact is pretty small even on elementary students who want to learn the subject; it must be infinitely smaller on masses at large. As I understand Northrup, he maintains the thesis that it was the causality principle of classical mechanics that was primarily responsible for the substitution of the Marxian philosophy for the earlier one of Locke. I just wonder, if for example the Heisenberg uncertainty principle and the corresponding abandonment of the causality principle had been available a hundred years ago, whether we wouldn't have communism in Russia today just the same.

In judging the merits of a planned economy versus one based on our more individualistic mode of life, I wonder if from the standpoint of the common man there isn't a very simple criterion, namely, which has the greater efficiency in production and distribution. Perhaps this is too mundane a philosophy, but I believe that it is a realistic one. If we could convince the people of Russia that the average man would have more telephones and more automobiles under our system of economy, I wonder how long their system of economy would last, and vice versa. However, in appraising the satisfactions involved in the different *modes de vie*, the right of a person to be left alone and to do as he pleases should be considered as one of the basic materialistic wants. Perhaps there is some other equal pleasure in a planned economy, but I don't know of it.

THE FOUNDATIONS
OF FREEDOM IN SCIENCE

MICHAEL POLANYI

TODAY the position of science is under reconsideration all over the world. We have seen a serious attempt made in Russia to control science on the lines of a Marxist philosophy. This movement has had repercussions in Britain where during the last ten years a great deal was heard about the necessity of planning science through some kind of central organization. In the United States similar tendencies seem to have arisen at the close of the recent war from a widespread desire to see the powers of science, which were so spectacularly demonstrated during the war, energetically applied to the needs of peace.

Whenever, as in these cases, the basic institutions of science are at issue, scientists will find it necessary to reconsider with care the need for freedom in science and there will arise a new interest in the deeper nature and justification of such freedom.

Issues far outside scientific life will help to foster this interest today. The value that men attach to freedom has plunged, in our generation, into a deep dive from which it is only now climbing precariously out again. Scientists may want to help the world on its way back to freedom by making known how freedom operates in science.

To the analysis of freedom in science I shall therefore turn now.

Freedom in science assigns to each mature professional scientist the task of conducting research with the aim of making the greatest possible contribution to science. Such a responsibility is a heavy one, but it is a free responsibility.

The mature scientist chooses his subject at his own discretion and pursues it day by day in the same discretionary manner. He draws his own conclusions and stakes such claims as he thinks right. At no point of his research work is he subject to any specific instructions from any superior authority.

Freedom of scientific research is in harmony with some intensely personal impulses. The choice of a problem, its pursuit and final conquest are manifestations of the individual scientist's passion for discovery. They bring into play intellectual powers which are otherwise hidden and assert creative forces of a unique kind. An individualist philosophy would regard these personal impulses as the justification for freedom in science. But I find such a view rather superficial. For, clearly, not every strong personal impulse can claim respect and it remains therefore to be shown why those of the scientist should be respected.

A more fundamental approach is gained by examining what may be called the coordinative functions of freedom in science. A statement submitted recently by Dr. Enrico Fermi to the Senate Hearings on Science Legislation defines this function as follows:

"Experience has indicated that the somewhat haphazard exploration of the field of knowledge that results from an intensive freedom of the individual scientific worker to choose his own subject is the only way to insure that no important line of attack is neglected."

We have here a plea for freedom in science on the ground of social efficiency. The discretionary powers which a system of freedom grants to scientists are said to constitute the only effective machinery for coordinating the efforts of individual scientists to the joint purpose of the advancement of science.

Now, one usually thinks of coordination as a process imposing restraint on the discretionary powers of individuals.

Much of my argument will be concerned therefore with finding out how coordination is achieved in science by the opposite method of releasing individual impulses.

A first step towards the answer is easy to find by throwing a glance at a group activity in which coordination is totally absent. Take a number of people shelling peas. There is no occasion here, and no possibility, to adjust the work of one person to the work of another, for the value of their total achievement is simply proportionate to the sum of the peas shelled by each. Science cannot be conducted by such isolated efforts. Supposing scientists were kept for a few hundred years strictly without any mutual communication, the total discoveries achieved by them would be little more than what is normally gained by science in a few years. No continued systematic growth of science would take place at all.

The coordinative principle of science is thus seen to consist in the adjustment of each scientist's activities to the results achieved by the others. Since such mutual adjustment depends on the independent decisions of each, its operations require the complete freedom of all.

It would seem that we are faced here with a basic principle leading quite generally to coordination without intervention of any coordinating authority. It is a simple principle of logic which can be demonstrated on quite trivial examples. Consider the piecing together of a jig-saw puzzle, and suppose we take a very large puzzle which would take one person a number of days to piece together. Assume further that we had a dozen players who would like to help. It would obviously be of little use to give to each player a separate set of the puzzle to work on in isolation, but it would greatly speed up the solution if all participants were allowed to work on the same set, each taking note of the results of the others and using them as their starting point.

The logic of this form of coordination can be reduced to

even simpler terms, for every mathematical calculation carried out by successive stages of approximation may be taken to illustrate it. Each step in such a computation deals with one phase of a problem at a time and relies at each step on the results of the earlier steps. This becomes particularly clear if we think of problems in which each step is operated at a different point in space. A common example of such a polycentric problem is the distortion of a rigid framework of joists pinned together at a large number of points. Given the elastic properties and the distribution of loads over all the pinpoints, the solution can be found by the "relaxation method" which consists in calculating the displacement of each pinpoint in turn in respect to its neighbors, the position of their neighbors being assumed for the moment as fixed. In passing from one center to the next the displacement previously calculated for the others is always taken into account. If a large number of such calculations had to be quickly made for a given rigid framework, we could employ a team of calculators, and place each in charge of one particular pinpoint. They could all go on working independently, merely notifying each other of their results and mutually taking these into account.

We have reduced here to the simplest terms the coordinative function of freedom. It seems to be based on the fact that in certain cases a joint task can be achieved by a group of participants who know not what the result of their joint efforts is to be and are not directed by anyone who knows it. The coordinative function of freedom in science would appear thus as merely an instance of the general logic of such spontaneous coordination; and scientific inquiry would be merely the pursuit of a peculiar kind of polycentric problem in which the participants happen to bring into play intensely personal impulses and an exceptional degree of creative judgment.

Such a conclusion, however, would be seriously incomplete, as it would fail to take into account the characteristic *vagueness* of the task pursued by science. The pieces of a jig-saw puzzle are bought in shops with the certainty that they will yield a solution known to the manufacturer. Processes of successive mathematical approximation advance towards a definitely foreseen end. Science does not proceed towards such predefined ends. In the sense in which there exists a task of piecing together a jig-saw puzzle, or of solving a polycentric mathematical problem, the task of science cannot be said to exist at all. If we want to understand spontaneous self-coordination in science we must yet discover in what sense there does exist a common task of science.

Our first reaction may be to look for a definition in terms of explicit premises underlying the scientific interpretation of nature. But there exists no strict set of suppositions on which scientists are agreed and have been agreed throughout the past centuries. Whatever premises may be held in common among scientists, they are not to be found formulated in definite precepts. They can therefore be said to exist only as implied in the practice of scientific inquiry. To the examination of this practice let us therefore turn.

I submit that the coherence of science is implied in every affirmation of discovery. A claim to discovery expresses the scientist's conviction of having gained an element of truth which other scientists are bound to recognize, and his claim is also usually based on his own recognition of discoveries made by other scientists. Moreover, every new discovery claims to form an addition to the system of science as transmitted from the past. There is inherent therefore in each new claim to discovery the practical affirmation of a coherent system of truth which is capable of indefinite extension into yet unexplored regions.

For the extension of this system scientists rely on methods embodied in the common practice of research. Scientists accept, utilize and transmit certain traditional procedures and standards. They uphold certain traditional ideals.

I conclude that the dedication of scientists to the advancement of an intellectual process beyond their control and to the upholding of values transmitted to them by tradition represents the sense in which science does possess and pursue a coherent task. Alternatively, we may express the existence of such a task by saying that scientists form a community believing in a certain spiritual reality and covenanted to the service of this reality.

Those who, whether within science or outside it, subscribe to these beliefs and underwrite this covenant affirm by implication the presence of a spontaneous coordination of independent creative impulses in science. They uphold the coherence of science and through it the freedom of science. Those who deny such metaphysical beliefs and repudiate such transcendent obligations deny by logical implication also the possibility of both self-coordination and freedom in science. They may not act by this logic, very often they do not, but the implication remains true all the same.

The organized forms of scientific life—publications, university posts, research grants, and scientific distinctions—form a system of opportunities, rewards, and restraints for the pursuit of science. This system is governed by scientific opinion. Scientific opinion prevents cranks, frauds, and habitual blunderers from gaining ground in science. At the same time it apportions credit to valid contributions, appraising and supporting their authors according to their merits. These disciplinary and administrative actions are indispensable to science cultivated today by thousands of contributors. By performing them, scientific opinion enforces the coherence of science, which is the basis of freedom in science.

We can clearly see now the inadequacy of the individualist theory of freedom in science. Individual impulses are not as such respected in science but only in so far as they are dedicated to the tradition of science and disciplined by the standards of science.

Modern science depends for its material existence on support from outside. Scientific opinion which watches over coherence and freedom within science cannot fulfill this function unless its decisions are respected outside science. In allocating their support to different scientific purposes, outside authorities must accept the guidance of scientific opinion. They would otherwise inevitably disrupt the coherence of science and undermine its freedom.

Such are the foundations of freedom in science. It is easy to see why they may be called in question in the world today. The autonomy of science cannot be recognized by any government whose official philosophy emphatically denies transcendent reality to science. Inevitably, such a government will come in conflict with the autonomy of science.

Similar dangers may arise more incidentally wherever the responsibility for the expansion of scientific institutions falls to public authorities who are not sufficiently familiar with the nature of science. As guardians of the public interest they may feel reluctant to leave to scientific opinion full control over public funds allocated to science. Dazzled perhaps by the achievements of applied science in wartime—which had, quite rightly, been placed under the direct control of the political authorities—they may fail to recognize clearly the different nature of the quieter pursuits of pure research and not realize that these can be maintained only in complete independence.

By defending the foundations of freedom in science we may help people to recover a clear conception of freedom in general. The theory of scientific freedom which I have just outlined might indeed be found capable of extension to other fields of social life. There are other realities of the mind besides science and there exist transcendent obligations other than those which are particular to the scientist. There exist great traditions which embody these realities and these obligations and which comprise all the main roots of our civilization. We have our tradition of intellectual honesty, which came to us from the Greeks; that of brotherhood, which we derived from Christianity; that of legal reason, which was the heritage of Rome; and that of tolerance which we were taught by Milton and Locke.

All these traditions form, like that of science, the premises for an indefinite sequence of individual creative actions—actions which are, or at least tend to be, spontaneously coherent, and which by their unrestrained interplay form the constitution and essence of a free society.

Therefore, the general foundations of coherence and freedom in society may be regarded secure to the extent to which men uphold their belief in the reality of truth, justice, charity, and tolerance, and accept dedication to the service of these realities, while society may be expected to disintegrate and fall into servitude when men deny, explain away, or even simply disregard these realities and transcendent obligations.

Disintegration may follow on the one hand the path of an individualistic theory of freedom, which, when consistently pursued, will result in romantic self-love coupled with civic indifference. Concurrently we may find that the institution of government is being increasingly interpreted in terms of sheer force and that history is represented as the process of one class liquidating another and one nation eliminating another. Such are the logical derivatives of an effective denial of transcendent values, and much of our own disasters can be readily described in these terms.

A radical denial of absolute obligations cannot destroy the moral passions of men, but it may render these passions homeless. The desire for justice and brotherhood can then no more confess itself for what it is. Consequently it seeks embodiment in some theory of salvation through violence. Thus we see arising those sceptical, hard-boiled, allegedly scientific forms of fanaticism which are so characteristic of our modern age.

Man's rapidly increasing destructive powers will soon put the ideas of our time to a crucial test. It seems that unless we radically reaffirm the transcendent foundations of our civilization, the logical outcome of their present inadequacy will not be delayed for long. A consistent vindication of freedom in science may point the way towards the necessary reaffirmation of our whole civilization.

DISCUSSION

TOLMAN: Polanyi's thoughtful words will receive the approval of scientists and of wise men in general. His analysis of the foundations of freedom in science has proceeded along the following lines.

Assuming a society which encourages the free organization of scientific work, he first emphasizes that each individual scientist is set free under such circumstances to choose those fields of investigation best suited to his own talents and enthusiasm, and in those fields to direct his day-by-day work without external direction. The importance of these conditions for releasing those strong personal impulses which are necessary for creative scientific work cannot be overestimated. But this cannot of itself be regarded as a justification for scientific freedom since not all strong personal impulses are worthy of respect.

But it is next pointed out by Polanyi that the freedom accorded to individual scientists does not imply uncoordinated activity, since each scientist adjusts his work to the results obtained by others and furnishes results which become the basis for the further work of others in the field. Scientific investigation thus becomes a unified activity resulting from the unenforced coordination of the free acts of individual scientists. The scientist is thereby absolved from the suspicion of using his freedom to follow merely willful personal impulses.

Nevertheless, it is then emphasized by Polanyi that this coordinated free activity, by its very nature as an attempt at discovery, must lead toward an unknown future outcome. This unknown outcome might conceivably be illusory and harmful. It is only through an extrapolation of past successes that we believe in the reality and value of the results of free scientific inquiry.

The justification for this extrapolation is regarded by Polanyi as the crucial difficulty in upholding the freedom of science. In making his justification, he places reliance on the continuity of scientific tradition to keep our endeavors essentially similar to those of Copernicus, Galileo, and Harvey. He emphasizes the role of scientific tradition in guiding research away from that which is routine and trivial and from that which is unfounded and fantastic, and in providing institutional opportunities for the encouragement of competent scientists and the discouragement of quacks. He also pays due attention to the temporarily disastrous consequences that have been brought about by recent attempts to replace the free organization of science by state control. He is thus led to his final conclusion "that freedom in science is a process of inherently coordinated spontaneity, founded on the assumption of a transcendent reality called science, which is embodied in a tradition to the cultivation of which scientists are dedicated." The acceptance of this conclusion, essentially by an act of faith, would give meaning to the pursuit of science and justification to the claims of scientists for freedom in their undertaking.

Polanyi closes by emphasizing that similar considerations and similar acts of faith might lead to a more general theory of the process of freedom as a state of inherently coordinated spontaneity, and to the reinstatement of other realities, such as justice and mercy, capable of guiding the free coordination of those who believe in them. In his own words, "We may be faced with the fact that only by resuming the great tradition which embodies faith in these realities can sufficient confidence be restored among men to make the continuance of the human race on earth, equipped with the powers of modern science, both possible and desirable."

I wish to make some brief remarks on three characteristics of science which have a bearing both on the general problem of the foundations of freedom in science, and on special problems that arise in an acute form from the control of scientific information in the interests of national and international security.

My first remark has to do with that characteristic of science which makes it possible, in a reasonably unambiguous way, to distinguish between pure science and its application to practical ends. This distinction has an important bearing on our general problem, since it seems clear to me, and is I think also Polanyi's opinion, that our justification for the freedom of science applies primarily to investigators in the field of pure science rather than to those engaged in developing its uses for practical ends. These practical ends may be beneficial or harmful—atomic energy for good and for evil—and it is clearly not the function of scientists to decide freely as scientists what is good and what is evil. Scientists do have the function of keeping others informed of the practical implications of their work. The distinction between pure and applied science also has an interesting bearing on the special problems that arise in connection with the declassification of secret military information. In this country it has been possible to adopt a national policy which in considerable measure releases to the public such information in the field of atomic energy as is purely scientific, but for the sake of national security retains for the present the classification of technical know-how directly connected with the production of fissionable materials or their utilization for military purposes.

My second remark has to do with the objectivity of science. This is the wonderful characteristic of science which make its results acceptable and of the same meaning to all who will take the time to study them. The objectivity of science has an important bearing on our general problem, since it is a necessary prerequisite for that unenforced co-ordination of the free acts of individual scientists which lies at the basis of Polanyi's theory of scientific freedom. The objectivity of science also has important bearings on special problems which are acute today. In this connection we emphasize the transcendent character of objectivity which recognizes no limitations or national boundaries. On the other hand, this transcendent character of objectivity helps to explain the unhappiness of scientists when in the interests of their country and of their convictions they have to accept limitations on free communication. Some scientists may be careless or confused in this matter, but for the most part they are glad to make this sacrifice at a time when others may have to make much more immediate sacrifices on the field of battle. But this transcendent character of objectivity holds a hope for the future, since thereby the scientists of all nations are provided with a common language and a common area of agreement from which further agreement may grow. In this connection it is noteworthy that in the proceedings of the United Nations Atomic Energy Commission it has so far been only in the meetings of the Scientific and Technical Committee that common agreement on any matters of substance has been reached by the representatives of the twelve nations.

My final remark has to do with the abstract character of science. In the present connection I am concerned with the necessary abstraction that has to be made in order to secure objectivity. Abstraction of those elements on which agreement can be reached and elimination of the remainder is part of the price that has to be paid for the objectivity of science. This circumstance has played a dominating role in meetings of the Scientific and Technical Committee of the Atomic Energy Commission, where an almost fantastic elimination of anything smelling of policy was necessary in order to secure unanimous agreement for the Committee's "Report on the Scientific and Technical Aspects of the Problem of Control."

BRIDGMAN: It is simply impossible to disagree with Polanyi's conclusion that freedom of science is necessary. At the same time, I find to my surprise that I am not willing to accept all of the reasoning by which he gets to this unassailable conclusion. I feel that he both includes more than is necessary and leaves out something which is essential.

I put the question thus: What is my relation to society and what is society's relation to me and what are the effects of science on this relation? I have to answer all these questions from my own point of view, because society is made up of the individual actions of individuals. As illustrated on this crude diagram (Fig. 3) I function in two respects, as an

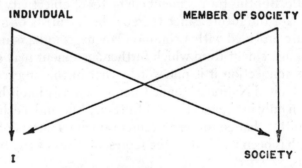

Figure 3. Bridgman's diagram

individual and as a member of society. As an individual I move by certain considerations of the effect of my actions on myself (arrow from *individual* to *I*), and also I move by consideration of the effect of my actions on society (arrow from *individual* to *society*). In my capacity as a member of society I am interested in the effects which my actions have on me as an individual and the effects which my actions have on society as a whole (these interactions are shown by the two other arrows). Among these four interactions or arrows, Polanyi in my opinion has thrown away the interaction between the *individual* and the *I*. As an individual I think that freedom of science is necessary, because what I can do in science is as real to me as anything physical. My relation to society as an individual is governed by certain responsibilities. I don't think it's right for society to support me unless I make corresponding returns to society. I imply that my scientific contribution to society justifies society in supporting me, and that would be because it is good to have people who are working to satisfy the passion for understanding and also because a considerable number of things which science produces are for the good of society.

Now envisaging myself as a member of society: I must consider whether science is worth supporting, whether physical science in particular is worth supporting. Science is worth supporting because of its effect on society. But also there is this other fact, that society owes certain obligations to its members. We must ask what society is for. It should offer to all of its members, to a certain degree, an opportunity for self-realization, and must provide these opportunities. I think that further postulates, however attractive with regard to these relations, are superfluous in the sense that we do not require them in order to justify the freedom of science. My final comment on Polanyi's theory is that it is not a minimal argument; it puts in considerations which are not necessary in order to draw his conclusions.

H. S. TAYLOR: I now ask the representative from Soviet

Russia whether he wishes to speak at the present time. Turkevich has consented to translate his remarks.

MESCHERYAKAV: What I wish to say I am saying extemporaneously as my personal opinion. It is also an aesthetic point of view. We must be thankful that we are living in an interesting world which has various distinctions, and that these diversities spring from our very foundations.

They exist in the sphere of nucleonics, in the ordinary world, and in our social relationships. The diversities in ideology, the differences in point of view are only another manifestation of the diversity of nature.

We can draw a clear connection between diversity in ideology and diversity in the world around us. We must try to do that. At the present moment, however, it is a very difficult task.

In spite of differences in ideology and points of view, we *do* recognize the existence of one fundamental point—the existence of a common philosophy of nature.

This one natural philosophy is just as correct in Russia as it is in the English-speaking countries, in China, in the other parts of the world. It is a very reassuring fact that among these diversities there is this agreement on a fundamental philosophy of nature. I consider the unifying idea of this natural philosophy as a symbol of the unity of the world. I think that in our troubled times this is a very hopeful sign.

To pit the Russian ideology against the Western ideology on the question of freedom of science is without foundation and without basis of fact. Creative processes are understood throughout the world to be free and independent.

H. S. TAYLOR: I beg Turkevich on behalf of this group to convey our best thanks to our Russian colleagues for their contribution to our discussion. On behalf of Princeton University I say that we are deeply gratified by this evidence of intellectual collaboration, the first which we have been able to secure in the western world since the cessation of hostilities in Europe; and I believe that we may welcome this as the initial stage in the process of reconciliation of scientists, philosophers, and social scientists which is the necessary preliminary to the reconstitution of one world.

E. B. WILSON: I should like to speak about Bridgman's diagram because I think that there has been a great deal of discussion about the social benefits of science which assumes that these always stem from the material achievements of science.

Now frankly, while I am much impressed by the telephone, etcetera, I think there is a much greater contribution of science to society, and that is cleansing the mind of superstition. It seems to me that unless one understands the universe, life is not worth living. One needs to have some appreciation of the fact that we have progressed from the mental attitude of the savage, where a demon lurks behind every bush, to the present where we are at least beginning to understand the sources of our troubles.

But how is all this connected with the necessity for freedom in scientific research? I suggest that the connection is that on one hand the investigator is primarily interested in pushing back the boundaries of ignorance, while on the other hand some non-scientist may be charged with the distribution of government funds for science, and this person may have in mind the material benefits only. Seldom will a non-scientist recognize as thoroughly as a scientist the non-material benefits of science, and therefore there is great danger that the suggested planning boards will distribute money in such a way as to discourage the pushing-back of the boundaries of ignorance and superstition for the sake of encouraging the production of material benefits.

CORYELL: Quoting from Polanyi: "Freedom of science assigns to each mature professional scientist the task of conducting research with the aim of making the greatest possible contribution to the advancement to science." I want to make an issue of this point. I agree that the scientists have an obligation to investigate the universe on an individual basis; but in the last few years many American scientists have felt that their obligations to society transcended that to science itself, not to speak of those other obligations we all have to our wives and children and to our department at the university. In this audience are many people who have given much thought to the social implications of atomic energy for modern war and for society; outside of this audience there are literally many hundreds of physicists and chemists, as well as men of other professions, who have done the same. This is a departure from the ivory tower tradition of pure science which, regrettable or not, is a characteristic of the time.

If I am correctly informed about Russia, a Russian is politically educated from the time he learns to speak, and simultaneously develops a feeling for the social implications of science. We who were on the atomic bomb project or related projects during the war experienced a similar sort of development in ourselves, and that development is obviously playing an important role in American science. It has counterparts in France and Great Britain, and I assume that a similar development will occur over much of the world.

MEES: I take issue with Tolman's description of applied science as a field in which freedom of science might conceivably be undesirable. I have been engaged in applied science for forty years, and in that period I have come very definitely to the conclusion that the prosecution of applied science in its most efficient form is identical with that of pure science. I don't think for a moment that it is desirable that applied science should be directed *except in times of emergency*. Emergencies arise in applied science frequently, just as they recently did in the applied science of war. There are occasions when the machines in the factory break down and we go to the scientists as a whole and ask them what they can do to get the machines operating again. Emergencies *do* arise; and when they do, it is usual to limit the freedom of the scientist, not by direction, but by appeal. That of course happened in the war. When the emergency came we appealed to the free scientists and they cooperated, working with each other and directing themselves and limiting their freedom to meet the emergency. But in normal times, when no emergency exists, we in the industrial laboratories should no more consider the limitation of our freedom than you would consider limitation in the university. At least, if we consider it, we ought to stop. I haven't the slightest doubt that the only successful way of conducting an industrial research laboratory over a long period is to find good men and leave them alone. That is the experience of all good laboratory directors. I have recently been making a study of the direction of laboratories, and I found that although various institutions thought that they had various systems for directing research, in practice they all did exactly the same, which was that they didn't do anything.

Something of the same thing arises in connection with our views of the Soviet scientists. We have had some suggestions that we should emulate the planning which is supposed to exist in Soviet science; these suggestions come from western scientists who have thought that all research should be controlled by a planned system. In practice, as far as I can find out from the descriptions that come from Soviet Russia, from the accounts which its scientists give of their work, they pursue their science in exactly the same way that we do—in complete freedom.

DuBridge: When society gives us freedom, society asks what we give in return. Polanyi's answer is that what we have to give is the assurance that we shall arrive at good coordination of science. I suggest that "coordination" is not a sufficient description of what is obtained, and I prefer the word "achievement." Science proceeds by driving salients forward; after the salients are made comes the process of coordinating them. Freedom of science gives science itself rather than simply coordination.

ALLISON: I believe so passionately in freedom of science and freedom of intercommunication between scientists that when I arise to discuss the matter I usually radiate more heat than light. Let me recall the point made so often during discussions: the trend of science and of physics in particular, involving the advent of large machines as tools of research, has a bearing on the question of freedom. It is not possible for a physics department to erect one of those machines without coordination of many able men working on the same problem. The minute you start coordinating, you circumscribe freedom to a certain extent. We are obliged to think and see what compromises we have to make with the idea of complete individual freedom in order to erect and use these huge new tools.

KISTIAKOWSKY: I feel that there is no great difference between so-called *applied* and so-called *fundamental* research from the point of view of the investigator. During the war years I enjoyed working on applied problems of explosives and some other things just as much as I had enjoyed the work without practical purpose which I had previously done at Harvard and hope to do again. The great contrast is not that of applied versus fundamental research, but that of independent versus coordinated research. The latter was done in war work, and also in industrial research. I admit that most of the industrial laboratory directors when asked whether they direct their subordinates will say they do not, but I reply: ask the subordinates!

MEES: I contend that the difference involved between the industrial laboratory and university is less than Kistiakowsky thinks. If he believes that there is no direction or control in universities he should ask the professors.

BLACKETT: Traditionally academic science has been quite unorganized and extraordinarily fertile. But now that in England we have to ask the government for money to do fundamental research because work of this sort is so expensive, we need some coordination between scientists. In so far as it is necessary to get resources from the government, as is actually necessary in England now, it is the scientists' duty to organize themselves so that they can advise on the amount of money required and its allocation. It is possible to act in an uncoordinated manner only if each scientist can obtain the requisite resources independently. The total amount of research which is done in a country, in the university or industrial research laboratory or in a military laboratory, must be a matter of national policy.

NEW VISTAS FOR INTELLIGENCE

P. W. BRIDGMAN

WE are all agreed that the invention of the atomic bomb has presented us with problems which must be solved within the next few decades if the survival of civilization is to be more than a matter of good luck. Nevertheless, in spite of the urgency of these problems, I venture to invite your attention to certain longer range considerations which are equally fundamental and which have an equal claim to the attention of some of us now, for the solution of the longer range difficulties requires a longer period of preparation and must also be initiated in the present. It seems to me evident enough that many of our present social difficulties have their origin in our previous failure to begin thinking about the problems far enough ahead.

The opening of the atomic age may well mark the end of the first chapter in our development of the physical sciences and our partial mastery of our physical environment. It is conventional to ascribe this mastery to the development of scientific method, and there has been much discussion of what the essence of the scientific method is. It appears to me, however, that it is easy to take too narrow a view in this matter. I like to say that there is no scientific method as such, but that the most vital feature of the scientist's procedure has been merely to do his utmost with his mind, *no holds barred*. This means in particular that no special privileges are accorded to authority or to tradition, that personal prejudices and predilections are carefully guarded against, that one makes continued check to assure oneself that one is not making mistakes, and that any line of inquiry will be followed that appears at all promising. All of these rules are applicable to any situation in which one has to obtain the right answer and all of them are only manifestations of intelligence. The so-called scientific method is merely a special case of the method of intelligence, and any apparently unique characteristics are to be explained by the nature of the subject matter rather than ascribed to the nature of the method itself. For example, the universal and profitable use of mathematics in the physical sciences is a consequence of the possibility of using a system of precise numerical measurement in describing the systems which are the subject matter of physical science. The subject matter of other disciplines is not so often adapted to description in numerical terms, so that mathematics plays a smaller role in such disciplines.

The second chapter in the application of intelligence may well deal with the application of intelligence to the problems of human relationships. There are many people, perhaps the majority, who are convinced that these problems cannot be solved by intelligence. Their attitudes may range from the downright belligerency of those who maintain that the only solution is to be found by some supernatural method to the apathetic despair of those who plead that intelligence has never got us anywhere in the past. I shall not attempt to argue with either of these groups, but I address myself without apology to that minority who have the intellectual morale to believe that a serious application of intelligence to the solution of social problems is worth attempting. I shall pause only long enough to remark that I would challenge the validity of the evidence on which the bellicose base their confidence in the efficacy of supernatural methods, and to point out to the apathetic despairers that the method of intelligence has never had a fair trial.

If we grant that science is merely a special case of the application of intelligence, we may reasonably anticipate that our experience with scientific problems can suggest profitable lines for the attack by intelligence on the infinitely more complex and difficult problems of human relationships. Let us consider some of the suggestions from this experience.

Perhaps most important of all, we have acquired by this experience some insight into the nature of the process of intelligence itself. The revisions of scientific concepts made necessary during this century by relativity theory and quantum mechanics have shown that a certain self-conscious sophistication is necessary about being intelligent. Intelligence has its techniques, and we must be intelligent about being intelligent.

In popular estimate, perhaps the most important characteristic of science is its impersonality or "objectivity." The necessity for impersonality arises not from prejudice against people as such but because of the irrelevance of personal reactions to the commonest enterprises of science, which are concerned mainly with our external environment. In addition there is the consideration that our emotions are too likely to distort our report of factual situations. The "objectivity" of science is usually considered to be a guarantee of its truth. There is much of importance in this point of view to which we might devote our discussion with profit. The connotation here is often that science is objective because it is "public," independent of the idiosyncracies of any particular individual. This aspect of the use of intelligence which constitutes science must not be pushed too far, however, nor allowed to obscure the essential role played by the individual in scientific activity. Science is not truly objective unless it recognizes its own subjective or individual aspects. For example, scientific proof, or the conviction of truth or correctness, is something which each individual has to experience for himself. A proof vicariously accepted is dead. This is generally recognized. No editor of a reputable scientific journal will accept an article unless it is so presented that the reader may repeat the experiment and check the conclusions for himself.

The participation of the individual is necessary in every process of intelligence, not merely in the processes of science. Intelligence can be given a meaning only in terms of the individual. It seems to me that this has a far-reaching significance not usually appreciated, for I believe that here is to be found perhaps the most compelling justification for democracy. Intelligence is based on the individual. An authoritarian society in which the individual is suppressed cannot, by the nature of intelligence, be characterized by *general* intelligence.

There is another and much wider sense in which an objective science must recognize subjective aspects. However objective a science may be, it is still subjective from the point of view of the human race as a whole. Every activity of science and intelligence is a human activity, which necessarily involves the cooperation of the human nervous system. This characteristic of all that we do is so universal that it is not usual for us to recognize its existence. Even worse, we may deny its existence and elaborate its denial into a scheme of philosophy. There is a tendency to do this even in physics. As an example, I mention the philosophy of general relativity theory as distinguished from its mathematical formulation which (it seems to me) is based on an attempt to transcend the inescapable human reference point. Or, in another direction, there is perhaps danger that the spectacular success of the theoretical physicist in contributing to the atomic bomb will make him forget the limitations of the processes which he has used and give him so much confidence that he may even feel that experimental check has become superfluous.

From the wider point of view, the history of most philosophy and religion and much of politics has been the history of an attempt to repudiate the inescapability of the human reference point by the erection of absolutes and transcendentals. Our whole social structure has been built on the widespread acceptance of such absolutes and transcendentals. The intellectual basis for this acceptance goes back far into the past and acquired perhaps its most self-conscious expression with the Greek philosophers. The urge to invent absolutes seems to be an artifact of the human intellectual structure. It doubtless has its pragmatic justification and at a certain stage of evolution may have been as necessary for survival as that other indispensable invention, the external world. But whatever the origin or the pragmatic justification for this urge, there are aspects of it which will not survive intelligent scrutiny, and once the scrutiny is made and doubt begins to spread, the foundations of our social structure begin to crumble. This very process is going on at present. To put it crudely, men no longer believe in hell, and without the belief they will not respond to the same arguments to action which were potent while they believed. This decay of vividness of the old absolutes and transcendentals has been mainly an intellectual affair, due to a growing recognition that the absolutes simply are not "true." The movement has been gaining momentum for perhaps several hundred years, at first underground and only now breaking into the open and threatening social revolution. This is truly a chain reaction; what initiated the reaction would be difficult to say, perhaps the Protestant Reformation or the formulation of positivistic philosophies. The relative time scale of the explosion may not be so different from that of the atomic bomb when the different size of the fundamental units is considered, a human being and a lifetime corresponding to an atom and the duration of an excited state.

One consequence of this chain reaction is of special importance in present society and may be at the bottom of the growing tendency to fascist ideals all over the world. The old philosophical arguments for the necessity of the freedom of the individual rested importantly on the nature of God and other absolutes. If the thesis is to be now maintained new arguments must be found; they may well be based on the relation of the individual to intelligence.

Until now the repudiation of the old absolutes and transcendentals has been almost entirely of a negative character. They are no longer accepted, and people are no longer moved by motives which presume their acceptance; but the repudiation is a repudiation in a vacuum, for there are no new motives to take the place of the old ones and no new insights to take the place of the ones we thought we had. Our first task is to convert this repudiation into something more positive and constructive. This reconstruction is the task before us now. It will be a long slow process to which we must devote nothing less than our maximum intellectual capacity.

Such a reconstruction may well begin with an attempt to acquire understanding of the immediate situation by painstaking analysis, without any definite visualization of all the steps by which this analysis may prepare for the final solution. We might perhaps begin by asking what was the precise meaning of the absolutes and transcendentals by which we formerly sought to guide our conduct. In searching for these meanings we may take over the technique by which modern physics discovered the meaning of its concepts.

This technique is to examine exactly what we do when we apply a concept in any concrete situation. For example, an examination of the concept of simultaneity by Einstein by an analysis of the process used to determine whether two events are simultaneous showed the concept to be relative in nature instead of absolute as had been uncritically supposed before the analysis was made. Such a method of analysis will show the predominantly verbal character of most of our absolutes. For instance, analysis will often disclose that we can check in only one way on the propriety of using in a complex situation some word with an absolute connotation—to wit, asking our colleagues whether they would use the same word. There is usually no other method which I alone could apply in a laboratory remote from any social contact. Furthermore, the situation itself to which the word is applied is only too often a purely verbal situation, arising because my colleagues and I would use the same language. Consistent analysis by this method will disclose the exceedingly complex nature of the verbal structure which human beings have erected. Man has always been the builder, not only of pyramids and Chinese walls, but of intellectual and verbal systems as well. These come to absorb his complete attention; within them he may live an entirely self-contained existence, forgetful of the natural world about him and content with the companionship of his fellows. It seems to me that no education should be considered complete until a vivid consciousness has been acquired of this situation. How seldom is this recognized as one of the ends of education!

The analysis of meanings should be extended to all the important terms of daily life. Because there is such a large verbal element in these terms, it will be found that people with different linguistic backgrounds give different meanings to ostensibly the same words. All students of language recognize that it is very seldom that an abstract word in one language has an exact equivalent in another. To attempt to clarify this situation by getting more precise correspondence in different languages may well lead to the next step in the systematic development of a program of intelligence.

This next step might be to find how far the common assumption is justified that men are fundamentally alike intellectually and can come to agreement. This has never been established by direct experiment, but is nevertheless basic to all social thinking. To what extent are different people capable of responding in the same way to the same situation? After a certain age do people lose their ability to make certain intellectual discriminations as they lose the ability to make certain speech sounds? It is obvious that people of different backgrounds will at first almost certainly respond differently to many situations. But to what extent is this incidental? To what extent may people of different cultural backgrounds be made to see each others' points of view and make the same responses? The answer is not at all obvious, because there are certainly intellectual differences and limitations which are deep-seated and real. For example, it is probable that only a small fraction of the human race is intellectually capable of reacting to the subtleties of logic of the *Principia Mathematica,* and it may well be that there are analogous intrinsic differences in other lines of intellectual activity. It is important to know what the limitations are and at what level it is safe to set the minimum that may be presupposed in social institutions.

I think we have been too complacent in the past in assuming that our diversities of opinion are not of fundamental significance. Diversities are symptomatic of something, and we do not know what. It is time that we analyzed our disagreements and found their significance. Have we a right to our bland assumption that the human race is intellectually all alike, or may there be truly irreconcilable points of view? It is a crying disgrace that after twenty-five hundred years of philosophy the philosophers cannot agree in their description of what it is that they disagree about. I think our campaign of intellectual rehabilitation might well begin by collecting small groups of about five people, with different intellectual interests, and shutting them up until they emerged with statements as to what they could agree on in matters of ordinary social concern. In cases of disagreement they would be required to find the focus of disagreement, and agree in their formulation of the nature of the disagreement.

A prerequisite to the functioning of such groups would

be a declaration of freedom from mental reservations by all the members. There must obviously be willingness to ask any question whatever with regard to any topic and to answer that question as honestly and completely as intellectually possible to the individual. That is, no holds are barred. A claim that certain types of topics must be exempt from analysis would automatically disqualify the maker of such a claim from participation, and at the same time would afford a pretty clear presumption as to the character of any opinions which he might hold on such topics.

The group having been properly constituted, its deliberations might well begin by assuring themselves that all are really using language in the same sense. The very minimum of agreement that should be exacted is agreement on description of what happens or of what is done when social situations are verbalized. Physical science could not have started before physical situations could be significantly described in such terms that they could be reproduced. Social science might well set for itself the same prerequisite of significant description. I believe that it is not now known to what extent significant description of social or economic phenomena is even possible. Significant description in the physical sciences is closely correlated with successful prediction. How few social or economic situations there are in which prediction is at present possible! An example of the present confusion is the recent break in the stock market—there were as many attempts at significant description of what caused the break as there were commentators. Although we may never achieve sufficient mastery to predict in social or economic situations as we do in physical situations, I believe that we have the right to demand that we be able to predict at least the words which we use to describe such situations.

The ultimate result of such a campaign of analysis would be the removal of misunderstandings as to meanings from the causes of human disagreements. I think that most of us would admit that plain misunderstanding of meaning is one of the most common and potent causes of conflict, and that with its removal our problems would be far on their way to solution.

The people who would be excluded from such a clarification of meanings would be those who have disqualified themselves from making the analysis by their claim that certain holds are barred. It may be that right here will be found an unreconcilable cleavage between human beings, namely between those who bar no holds and those who bar some. If so, this method of attack will at least bring the situation out into the open where it can be better dealt with. The greatest difficulty here is that those who bar certain holds do not like to admit it openly. Part of the problem before us is to generate such a climate of public opinion that those who bar certain holds will feel themselves under pressure to admit it openly. They would certainly also try to justify themselves, and this would be all to the good in the way of clarification.

When the misunderstandings which arise from ambiguous meanings have been removed as a source of human friction, the next task for intelligence is an analysis of the implications and presuppositions of various social systems, in particular the social systems of the present. One of the lessons made vivid by the war was that in this country there is almost no self-conscious recognition of the necessary conditions of existence of a democracy like that of our ostensible ideal. There is great haziness in our ideas of the relation of the individual to his fellows. What are the minimum codes of conduct, which if universally accepted, would lead to a stable society in which conditions of living would be sufficiently tolerable? No systematic discussion is given of this question. The solution is usually attempted by some method more specialized than the minimum, as, for example, by exhorting everyone to live with complete unselfishness, putting the good of the whole in all cases unquestioningly above his own good. Universal acceptance of this exhortation would doubtless lead to a society appearing harmonious to a visitor from Mars. It is, however, a lazy man's solution, which begs the main questions at issue. Such a lazy man's solution is likely to conceal a metaphysical conception of society, ascribing to it an existence of its own apart from the indi- viduals who compose it, and ascribing a meaning to the good of this superthing. Such a view of the nature of society as a whole may be eliminated by an analysis of what one would have to do to prove the existence of such a superthing. The solution and the justification must be found in the individ- uals.

The importance of finding a minimum solution is obvious, for any solution more specialized than the minimum involves the imposition by force of the views of certain pressure groups of individuals on other groups of individuals in- capable of exerting as strong a pressure. Since a pressure group is itself composed of individuals and functions only through the functioning of its members, the discussion will involve norms of conduct and the ethics of the behavior of individuals in their capacity as members of groups. It seems to me that it is perhaps here that our general social con- sciousness is in its most primitive state of development. It is seldom indeed that an individual realizes that when he func- tions as a member of a pressure group his conduct demands special scrutiny, but he is nearly always willing to accept blithely the maximum that the group can obtain by the exercise of naked brute force.

Any discussion of the conditions basic to living together in society will lead inevitably to considerations of norms of conduct, ethics, purposes, and values. Now these are pre- cisely topics which the popular view holds are outside the scope of the methods of science. In so far as the methods of science are methods of intelligence, a corollary would be that questions of value are also not to be answered by the general processes of intelligence. There is a sense in which this contention may be maintained, for the task of intelligence may be regarded as merely to find methods of realizing the values which are presented to it from some external source. This view, while perhaps justified from the point of view of a narrow methodology, certainly overlooks features in the total situations in which values present themselves. For values are not static, but are subject to evolution and to education. The value which we ascribe to a course of action depends on the consequences of the action, and a more vivid realization of the consequences may lead to an alteration in the value ascribed to it. But a vivid appraisal of consequences demands intelligence. Rather than admit impotence in the field of values, it seems to me that just here is one of the most important arenas for the exercise of intelligence, in purging and educating our values.

It will perhaps be not too difficult for anyone to yield formal assent to the justifiability of much of what I have been saying. It will not, however, be easy for him to have a living quickening sense of all that is involved, of the shortness of the path that the human race has trod already, of the magnitude of the reformations necessary, and of the enormous potentialities in the future. Practically all conventional human thinking which deals with abstractions is cluttered with the debris from the past of absolutes and realities and essences. These abstractions are ingrained in all conventional thinking about human institutions, and all must be revised. It seems to me that no scheme of education is adequate to our modern needs which does not instill as its most important ingredient a realization of this situation. I for one am not willing to admit that a man has been liberally educated for a free society who has not learned to view instinctively the doings of men against the background of the potentialities of the future rather than of the incoherencies of the past.

DISCUSSION

KRAMERS: Bridgman has given us a very useful analysis of the benefits which the activities of human intelligence may have in store for us hereafter. There is one point to which I should like to draw attention. Intelligence is not everything, and in a more ideal behavior of mankind than the past has exhibited or the present exhibits, we should surely find many aspects not of a strictly intellectual nature. Imagine two people living together perforce on an island which does not yield food enough for two; their divergences of opinion about what is to be done can hardly be brought to disappear through improving the application of their intelligence. In spite of such cases, I agree that often a better application of intelligence will help materially in bringing about mutual understanding and cooperative effort.

Bridgman's suggestion that groups of people should come together to make a systematic analysis and definition of their words and concepts reminds me of the science "Significa" advocated thirty or forty years ago by a group of Dutch scientists, including the mathematicians Mannoury and Brouwer. These people pursued their aim earnestly and honestly for a long time, but attained only a moderate success; and their partial failure is not, in my view, entirely due to the inability of others to grasp the importance of their aim or the unwillingness of others to join in the pursuit. My own pet notion is that in the world of human thought generally, and in physical science particularly, the most important and most fruitful concepts are those to which it is impossible to attach a well-defined meaning. Take the concept of energy, for example. We can say just exactly why it was introduced and how it should be applied in one situation and another; but when we try to extrapolate its meaning, we find ourselves confronted with a program of investigation, and we do not know where it will lead us when we try to extend our concept into new domains. Another example is the verb "to be"; its meaning has a vagueness which is catastrophic for certain types of discussion, yet on the whole must be considered as natural and welcome.

The developments of relativity theory and quantum theory have certainly an important bearing on the problem and give new vistas for intelligence. But this newness is very old, as far as I can attach a meaning to the concept of intelligence. It is the old and almost trivial lesson that one can always learn more about certain things. This is taught anew to us by every new development in science. Our eyes remain the same, even when gradually they come to overlook wider and wider horizons.

MAYER: In connection with Bridgman's remark on the influence of verbal usage on our ways of thinking, I would like to suggest that our social sciences would benefit if we had a language in which the adjectives and words which are used to describe a society and to describe a nation were completely independent of the words which are used to describe an individual, so that there would not be the continuous confusion between motives and morality that are applicable to the individual and those concepts which we continually employ to describe the reactions of nations and groups.

RUSSELL: I was most interested in what Bridgman said about the use of words, but I think we may sometimes have a collision with the humanities, because humanists often seem to use words without rigorously defining their meanings. I think that probably the most ambiguous word in the English language is the word "spirit." But we have three unambiguous adjectives—spiritual, spirited, and spirituous! It's

going to be terribly difficult to get this cleared up, and I'm
not sure that we may not get into trouble even by attempting
it. Should we assume that the language which is used to
describe the conduct of groups (and how large a group is not
stated) ought to be entirely different from that used to
describe the conduct of an individual? Is it a safe assumption
that the relationships which exist between groups and on
which ethical principles are based are so different from those
which exist between individuals that it is desirable to use
different language? If they are not so different, if for example the relations between a couple or a simple family
and another couple and a simple family, are like those between individuals, is it not desirable to use the same or
modified words? I say this simply to illustrate the difficulties
of the problem, and I hope that someone wiser than I can
say more.

STEWART: I will develop one of Bridgman's proposals, the
suggestion that a certain number of individuals representing
certain disciplines or different pursuits might be brought
together to work for a considerable time to try to agree on a
statement of common principles. For example, I suppose he
might have had in mind a group including a physicist, a
mathematician, a philosopher, a biologist, a geographer, and
an historian of ideas, to bring the total up to six. Now at this
conference we are trying something not entirely unlike what
Bridgman has in mind, and some people have felt that our
discussions (apart from those on nuclear physics) have been
quite soft and even at times somewhat windy. This disadvantage, I am sure, is due to lack of coordination. The
general idea that a group of people representing various
disciplines get together and try to agree on a statement of
common principles may be traced back to Leibnitz (born in
1646). It has been ignored and people have actually been
hostile to it for more than two centuries. Future historians
may deem our apathy toward the idea as inexplicable as we

now deem the indifference of the dark ages toward the experimental method in natural science. I suggest that Bridgman's scheme be taken up and realized by some university or some foundation.

NORTHROP: I think the merit of Bridgman's paper is obvious. This merit is that we do need to find a common meaning for any concepts of the social sciences. The next question is, where are we going to find it? I take it that the thesis of this paper is that we are to find such meanings in denotatively given operations. There is truth in this contention, but there are also some difficulties. And I think that the difficulties center in the difference between the judgments in science of the experimental physicist and those of the theoretical physicist. What all are seeking is a constant or absolute meaning, the same through diverse subjective opinions. If this is so, it might be better to say that what Bridgman is arguing for is a constant or absolute meaning identified with denotatively given operations, rather than identified with some other operations such as a theoretical physicist might use. The trouble with a denotatively given operation is that it is questionable whether we do find common or constant meanings given denotatively.

For example, there is a story that has gone the rounds in my own university to the effect that certain social scientists set up a large calculating machine and then put statistical material in it. From the machine came a very remarkable answer which was supposed to be so important to society that it was telegraphed to Washington. Shortly afterward the social scientists found that the wires in the machine were crossed. Now what is the criterion of the wires in the machine being crossed? Why wasn't pushing the switch, and getting a repeatable result, an experiment? It seems to me that a denotatively given operation never answers that question. Only theory tells one whether the wires in the machine are to be connected in one way or another. Thus one has the

question of what concepts we use to designate and analyze
the denotatively given operation. This means, however, that
the theory or concept is defining the operation; not the
operation the concept.

And that raises the question as to whether you may not
have to go for common meaning—so that we may agree on
what we are talking about—to a source of meaning that is
given more in terms of the primitive concept of logic and
mathematics and deductive postulational technique than
in the realm of denotatively given empirical meaning. Leibnitz would maintain exactly this: that the only place one can
find common meaning is in a theoretically designated realm
constructed in terms of the primitive concepts of logic and
mathematics.

I think that the operational theory of concepts is one of
the most ambiguous theories that has ever been brought
forth. Of course, it always seems to work and the denotatively given operation seems to define the concept. Nevertheless, I believe that this occurs only if one smuggles a con-
ceptual interpretation into the denotative operation.

A man has an apparatus. He presses the switch and gets
a certain result. There is nothing in the operation that tells
whether the wires are crossed or not. It is the conceptualiza-
tion of the data necessary to bring them together into a consistent idea of what is in front of you that tells whether it is
a real experiment or one performed by someone who does
not know what he is doing. What is necessary here to get
out of this difficulty in the operational technique of clarify-
ing meaning is the introduction of an important distinction.
I feel that scientific theory and philosophical theory are shot
through with ambiguity because this distinction has not
received due attention.

We need to draw a very sharp distinction between concepts of two fundamentally different kinds in our sciences.
The physicists have succeeded in doing this, and I think this

is the reason you are so successful while other scientists are not. It isn't just that you have done experiments; it is that you clearly distinguish denotatively given terms of your experiments from theoretically given concepts, and you have learned how to correlate your theoretical concepts with your denotatively given ones. I prefer to call them "concepts by intuition" and "concepts by postulation." In the case of the theoretical concepts, you never find meaning by looking at things; instead they have meaning only in terms of a deductive system, a set of postulates. Thus you mean, for example, in the case of the concept "electron" that it is an entity satisfying the formal mathematical equations of the postulates and theorems of quantum mechanics. This is quite a different meaning from, for example, "blue" in the sense of color. "Blue" in the sense of color is a concept by intuition; "blue" in the sense of a wavelength in electromagnetic theory is a concept by postulation.

An apparatus and an operation becomes scientifically significant—so that you know whether it's a real experiment done intelligently or whether it's done by blindly throwing switches—only when you use conceptually defined types of meaning and postulational techniques. Hence the real success of physical science is owing to the fact that physicists distinguish these two kinds of things. That is why you require pure mathematicians and theoretical physicists as well as experimentalists. But in social sciences, especially in psychology and also in much philosophy, these two worlds of discourse become muddled together in the same language and produce nonsense.

It seems to me, therefore, that what Bridgman is arguing for is on the right track, but in order to carry it through one must pay attention to logically and postulatively prescribed meanings as well as to denotatively given meanings, and this will call for the operations of the mathematical and the theoretical scientist as well as for the experimentalist.

BRIDGMAN: I don't want to get into a technical discussion of what I mean by "operational," but I certainly wouldn't accept it as a synonym for "purely descriptive." I am perfectly aware that in the case of the calculating machine you would have to repeat a thousand times. I have never claimed that the operational description gave a complete picture, neither did I say that the mathematicians could give a complete answer to the world's difficulties. I think that what I described is necessary procedure, but I admit that you have to do more things than just that.

CORYELL: I believe there is experimental evidence for group intelligence. I also feel personally, without having gone through the analysis that Professor Bridgman describes as necessary, that there is some evidence of group intelligence and group personality among humans. In this regard I think that scientists often act as a group. I know by interpolation and extrapolation that I can speak as a scientist in a way that will be offensive to very few scientists, and I have done this in science reasonably well. I spoke yesterday for a group of about seventy-five people interested in fission products and I doubt that there will be very much objection to what I said. Of course this was technical information. I have also worked in connection with other groups in quite different manner. For example the great force of the Oak Ridge group in atomic energy politics was due to the fact that we had a working pact that any man could speak for the group if he checked his thoughts or letter or speech with one other man in the group. There were no examples of quarrels or divergences within the group, and we were very powerful in the national political scene last fall because of this group cooperation and with this group intelligence.

HAWKINS: In conversing with philosophers and scientists and just plain ordinary people I have heard people talk what I regard as good sense, and these were in almost every case people with whom I had not engaged in any previous discussions on the meaning of words. This fact seems to me to be in some contradiction to the emphasis on the necessity for engaging in such discussions. I realize that it is very important that we understand the meanings of our words, that is, understand what we are talking about; but the occasions when it is useful to discuss words occur not when we take a word out of the dictionary but when we are engaged with some real problem together with other people, and we find in the process that we are in difficulties because our theoretical interpretations are getting us into frequent contradictions. It is at this point that we should ask ourselves, like Bridgman, "What am I doing, why am I here, what is my purpose, and what sense can I make out of this or that kind of question?" I think it is clear also when we do this that there is a background of what the psychologists used to call apperceptive mass, of meanings which are not then and there in question, and without which we would be unable to go on. In any particular case where we really know something about what we are doing, where we have brought to the problem all of the ordinary garden variety of intelligence and language, and still we get into non-empirical difficulty, then at that precise point I think we can to some real advantage examine the meaning of particular words. But I feel that to separate this process from the process of trying to find out about the world we live in and what we should try to do about it cannot but lead to a new and most sterile scholasticism.

BRIDGMAN: I don't think that the analysis of words that I had in mind could possibly lead to such a situation. Such a group of five as I have postulated wouldn't get very far unless it had the proper kind of leader. He would attempt to point out the meaning of a word and ask the members of the group to prove that they had a right to the use of the word. Analysis would improve what I understand by the meaning of a word. It wouldn't be a mere question of the meaning of the word itself, and it wouldn't be a sterile investigation.

CORYELL: I would like to point out that here in these meetings is an example of the group intelligence of which I was speaking; this group intelligence has been applied to specific problems and I think that it has served to clarify many of the points involved.

H. S. TAYLOR: I agree with Coryell that this group has demonstrated a kind of group intelligence; as scientists we have a common point of view and are concerned with common problems, and our approach to these problems shows characteristic special attitudes toward problems of human values. These human values are intimately related to our view of the world as seen from the standpoint of science. We are all concerned for the future of education in science, research in universities and in large government laboratories, the scientific societies, and freedom of scientific expression, and we are concerned with the relations of these to other broader social and political problems. Most of us have struggled long with these questions within the scope of our personal relations, but recent events have thrust upon us a greater responsibility to clarify these relations and to make science contribute as much as possible to solution of the world's human problems. We are glad to assume this responsibility. Although physical science deals with the inanimate, the non-human, materials of the world, I believe that I can safely speak for this international group of physical scientists in saying that we believe that the human values of science, as well as its material accomplishments, can contribute significantly to the solution of the broad problems with which the world is faced.

THE IVORY TOWER
AND THE IVORY GATE

HENRY NORRIS RUSSELL [1]

WE have all heard plenty about the Ivory Tower in the past few years—as a place of refuge from unpleasant reality, and still more disagreeable obligations. The Ivory Tower Gate has been almost forgotten. There are two gates of Sleep. Out of the Ivory Gate come the false dreams, and from the Gate of Horn the true. Vergil was wise when he made the false dreams issue from the prettier gate. We know this still to our cost.

The first reaction of the modern man is to say, "We will destroy the ivory towers, and close the ivory gate." My thesis is that we should not do the first and cannot do the second. The last point needs little argument. Men will be free from false dreams only when they never dream at all. For this I have no hope, and upon reflection, very little desire. There is no such easy way. We must continue to judge our dreams, and reject what is false in them.

But why preserve the Ivory Tower? We would be better off without it if it were "the squat round turret, blind as the fool's heart"—but that was the Dark Tower. The true Ivory Tower has windows and a door. Its denizens may look out and see the world without, and sally forth into it "when duty calls, or danger," and for the common affairs of life. Is it worth while that they should have a place of retreat and refreshment when off-duty? I maintain that it is, and that the possession of such a refuge is an aid to men of science

---

[1] Professor Russell's paper was presented at a special session of the conference which was open to the public, and no arrangements were made for extemporaneous discussion.

in developing, maintaining, and restoring good international relations.

I choose examples from my own field of work, because we astronomers have perhaps the only ivory tower that still stands. It is our happy lot to deal professionally with matters remote from human affairs and human quarrels. Here and there we touch upon something "restricted"—for example, the relations between solar activity and radio transmission—but almost always we may pursue our researches with little hope of material profit to ourselves or others from their results, or fear of injury to anyone.

We have left our tower during the past troubled years, as duty called and circumstance allowed. We shall return to it joyfully, so far and so long as circumstance and duty permit.

For this very reason we astronomers find that we have a special opportunity to help in the restoration of international cooperation and good will. Cooperation is easy inside an ivory tower, if the occupants care more for their work, which *is* the tower, than for personal glory; and cooperation in the study of the external universe has long been forced on us by the very nature of the thing. A star-catalogue or orbit-calculation which rejected any data except those provided by some national, racial, or ideological group would be ridiculous. If our result is to have any claim to being definitive, we must take account of all the observations. We must study them, weight down the poor ones, and reject the bad; but the rules for doing this have the proverbial objectivity of mathematics and play no favorites.

Individual observers and observatories publish their own observations or catalogues based on them, not only to make them available to others but in the expectation that the minute personal and systematic errors which are inevitably present may be detected and eliminated by comparison with the results of others, perhaps a generation or two later. This is, of course, the spirit of science generally.

We have another advantage in the enormous number of bodies which have to be observed and of observations that must be made. Observations of a thousand stars might be made at one observatory; but when accurate positions of hundreds of thousands are needed, team-work becomes a necessity. Many cooperative undertakings of this type have been completed and some are still under way. The larger ones have included many observatories in both hemispheres and have taken decades to complete.

To secure a continuous record (so far as possible) of solar phenomena, observations in many places are required, not merely to diminish losses due to bad weather, but to be sure that at least one observer is on the sunward side of the earth when something happens.

There are taxonomic problems, too. When a star, for example, has been proved to be variable, it must be given a designation for ready reference. It does not matter whether this is provided by means of a name (as in the biological sciences) or by a combination of letters prefixed to the name of a constellation; it is vital that there shall be one internationally accepted designation for each object.

Standards of weights and measures and the like have also long been adopted by international agreement. The astronomers have had an active part in the preparation of standards of wave-length.

International commissions upon these matters functioned efficiently for many years before the war, and there seems not even to have been a suggestion that any local or nationalistic scheme should replace them in future.

Computing astronomers, in the offices of the various national ephemerides, have long shared the heavy labor of detailed prediction of the position of the sun, moon, the planets, and their satellites, and the "clock stars" used in observation for time. The American Ephemeris for 1940, for example, includes results of calculations made at Greenwich, Paris, Berlin, Madrid, and Washington. The exchange agreement has always wisely provided that such calculations as are necessary to provide the tables used by navigators should be made independently in each country.

Not everyone may know that this cooperative scheme survived through both World Wars, although it was one between government offices, data being communicated through neutral channels. The American Ephemeris, for example, published data computed in Paris up to 1943 and in Berlin up to 1945. These dates afford dramatic evidence that not the existence of hostilities but the fortunes of war brought the end. Ephemerides of the satellites of Saturn, to be sure, concern mundane affairs very little. They belong by right in the Ivory Tower, but they have not come through the Ivory Gate. Numerically, they are as accurate as we can make them, but they illustrate a truth of a different kind—that human cooperation may not only revive after a great war, but persist through it.

One more thing conspired to make astronomers a worldwide brotherhood. We are not numerous, only a few hundred active workers in all, and every serious reader of our literature knows the great majority of these by name and by their work. Within national limits the meetings of astronomical societies provide good opportunity for knowing one another—best, perhaps, in England, where the Royal Astronomical Society meets every month except in summer, but successfully here, where the American Astronomical Society, deliberately holding successive meetings in different parts of the country, affords opportunities for more than local acquaintance. The great international meetings, surprisingly well attended, extended this privilege world-wide. Forgive me if I recall with some nostalgia a meeting of the International Solar Union in Bonn in 1913. The list of members extended, if not traditionally from China to Peru, at least from Japan to Mexico. The business of the conference was effectively done, but what stands out clearest in memory is the final dinner on a Rhine steamer, with speakers in a dozen languages, and complete good will among us all. Looking back at it, it *may* have been rather an ivory tower—we did see a Zeppelin, but it came by courtesy, on a special exhibition flight for our benefit. Many of us had never seen aircraft in flight before!

But among ourselves at least the brotherhood was real, the fellowship genuine; and it is good to remember it and make it a cause for hope.

Next year the fancied millennium ended. Satan broke out of the Pit, and the nations went to war. But even then, the ties of scientific good will were not utterly broken.

In the critical week of 1914, when declarations of war filled the newspapers, Seeliger, then president of the Astronomische Gesellschaft, announced the abandonment of the meeting scheduled in Russia a few weeks later in the words "Wegen die herrschenden politischen Verwicklungen wind die Sammlung in Sankt-Petersburg nicht stattfinden." Could anything surpass this for courteous under statement?

Karl Schwarzschild, the greatest German astronomer of his day, entered his country's service as an officer. All who knew him were certain that his motives were honorable, however much we disagreed with him. A year or so later he was stationed at Namur. Whenever he could get away, he went to see the Belgian astronomers interned at Uccle. One of them told me afterwards, "Schwarzschild completely disarmed me." His freedom from enmity and his enthusiasm for science made him a welcome visitor. On his last visit he was walking in the Observatory garden and telling his enemy in law, but colleague in spirit, of his work on the distribution of brightness on the sun's disk. Wishing to draw a diagram, he found neither paper nor pencil. With a sudden inspiration, he drew his sword and scratched the curves in the earth of the path. As he sheathed it he said meditatively "Das Ding kann auch fur etwas vernünftiges benutzt werden." I know of no more poignant expression of an honorable man's disillusionment.

Had Schwarzschild lived he could have been of more help than anyone else in getting things to rights. But, alas, he was a Jew; hostile Junkers sent him to unhealthy duty on the Eastern Front, and he did not survive to see the armistice. Nevertheless, the restoration came, slowly but surely. The revived Astronomical Union met every three years in various countries. German astronomers were gradually co-opted on its committees, and in time Germany would have been formally admitted as a full member of the organization if it had not been for a new issue, which sounds quite modern today. There were five German Academies of Science, hence Germany demanded five votes, though France, Britain, and the United States had one apiece! By the time we met in Stockholm in 1938, many German astronomers attended, among them Professor Ludendorff, brother of the Kaiser's general. I can still see and hear, in memory, a French astronomer rising from his chair at the banquet, raising his glass to Ludendorff and greeting him by name.

This time the ivory walls were too thin to keep out all sound of the approaching storm, and there have been no great international gatherings of astronomers since.

But even during the war scientific communication did not wholly cease. A Committee on the Distribution of Astronomical Literature, working through neutral connections, found that a good deal of the published material was so free of information of possible military interest that it could be passed through the double censorship, outgoing and incoming. Abstracts of this, and originals sent on loan to interested workers, enabled Americans to learn of much that had been done not only in neutral countries such as Sweden and Switzerland, but in the occupied countries, and even in Germany itself.

With the end of hostilities progress has been rapid. The *Annales d'Astrophysique,* a purely French journal before the war, has received acceptances from a group of collaborating editors in several countries, including Abetti, an Italian though never a Fascist, who was invited but a few months after the German surrender. The last issue contains papers by a Finnish astronomer in Helsinki and a German in Freiburg, in the French zone of occupation. This is not so bad for the first year!

The International Astronomical Union is very far from being comatose. Its executive committee met in Copenhagen last March with delegates from thirteen countries, including the Big Four, and found extensive rehabilitation already possible. One of the most urgent needs was to catch up with several years' arrears of work in the nomenclature and cataloguing of variable stars, asteroids, etc. Most of this work had previously been done, and done well, by the Germans. A good deal of it has been returned to their hands, other parts have been taken over by the Russians, and some in this country. The cooperative spirit was strong; for example, the Russians volunteered to have the catalogues prepared under their supervision published in English. The *Astronomischer Jahresbericht,* published annually and containing abstracts of the world's publications in the whole field of astronomy, will be prepared at Heidelberg, with the full support of the American authorities of occupation, and the forwarding of the literature to be abstracted will be managed through Greenwich by the Astronomer Royal.

When transportation and housing conditions permit, the full meetings will be resumed.

The world's astronomers are not wiser, or better, or more friendly than other men. If they have made a good start, it is largely because their ivory tower has been a refuge where one group of common interests has been able to survive. Without sacrificing our own convictions or anyone else's, and without appeasement, we have already been able to get a great part of the old cooperation in action, and we can be confident of rebuilding far more in good time.

There are many areas in which our colleagues in other sciences are already busy in the same good work. The international rules and committees for nomenclature, often regarded as necessary nuisances, will now serve as unifying links. The same is true of those bodies which establish international standards of any kind. Even in the most seriously restricted fields, such as physics, there are free areas, and within them the process of restoration will begin. The basic principles of scientific cooperation, and the spirit in which it was once carried on and can be carried on again, are essentially the same. Personal relations between individuals will depend upon past records and present convictions; but this has always been true, and ought to be.

I conclude, then, that ivory towers have still a useful function to perform. They are not meant for permanent residences, nor for hidey-holes in time of trouble. But they can be the abodes and sometimes the preservers of community and good will. One remembers the "Mother-Lodge."

"Outside: Sergeant! Sir! Salute! Salaam!

Inside: Brother, and it ain't no 'arm."

My plea is for the preservation of a certain esoteric quality of science, and in each particular science, born of common interests and a common way of thought which binds its votaries into a fellowship independent of their other connections. This is a unifying influence and a much needed antidote against the mass-psychology and herd-loyalties that torment the world.

We need this in national and social as well as in international affairs. I believe that science and the body politic may both be injured by listening to the enthusiasts who strive for the participation of science, as such, on either side of the divisions raised by political or social ideologies. Our learned and professional societies have here a special obligation to be impartial. Their members can and ought, as citizens, to take sides actively in hot debates and close votes. But the case should be very clear indeed before they make bold to commit science itself.

This is no academic matter. Measures for the support of science have recently been before Congress. They dealt with intricate problems, some of which, such as patents, involved general economic and social questions rather than the specific interests of science; and legislation including several little-correlated fields was often included in one bill. Wide differences of opinion inevitably arose among men of science regarding the relative desirability of this or that course of action, or of no action at present. As citizens many of them campaigned vigorously for their convictions, but it is fortunate that our scientific associations refrained from taking sides, as organized bodies, upon questions which were essentially political.

A measure which proposed to put the choice of those scientific projects which were to be supported in future in the hands of a group the majority of whose members had no scientific knowledge would have been another matter. We should have had to oppose that.

There are many times when we must come out of our ivory towers and fight in the name of science and for its sake —for example, against the perennial campaigns of sentimentalists opposed to medical research upon animals. But we have worse enemies now—things that once came out of the Ivory Gate as false or foolish dreams, and have grown into vast ideological systems supported intellectually by ingenious tissues of special pleading and half-truths, mingled with deliberate falsehoods, and materially by all the resources of naked power. Here, as men of science, we have a great responsibility. We and we alone can expose and refute the twisted theories of race and class and meet the specious claims of a degenerate science by insistence upon the actual facts and unbiased analysis of them. Those who heard it will not soon forget the intense cold passion of Archibald Mac-Leish's indictment, after the war had begun but before we were in it, of the writers and scholars, who, absorbed in their own interests, had failed to use their weapons of spoken and written words against these deadly sophistries until it was too late. Our ivory towers then were too often the abodes of negligence and blindness.

Victory in the field has not removed these perils, nor our obligation. New delusions are thronging out of the Ivory Gate. As scholars as well as citizens we must be on guard. We need the scientific spirit, the impartial investigation of the facts and assessment of the degree of reliability of the conclusions which we draw from our data, the keen, dispassionate, ruthless study of the merits and defects, the successes and failures of our own theories and of other people's, the objective and thorough examination of proposals for the application of these theories, and above all, incessant watchfulness against wishful thinking.

We may anticipate honest and sincere disagreement, both in theory and on policy; but we may at least agree upon the importance of controls upon our experiments and on the unwisdom of putting new schemes into effect on a grand scale until they have been tested in the pilot-plant stage. We may well believe that in these ways and in others we are fitted to be of help in the present and the immediate future. But it behooves us to take heed lest having saved others, we ourselves may be castaways.

Dreams from the Ivory Gate come to all men; if we think ourselves immune, we invite them. It is of what seems to me to be such a dream that I would speak in closing. There has been much discussion of late about the freedom of science and of the scientific worker. The wartime restrictions now in process of relaxation have left a spirit of resentment and raised a problem which it is our duty to consider thoroughly and most seriously. The question is this: should the scientific investigator be free, on his own recognizance, to experiment on any subject and to any extent that he personally sees fit, and to publish his findings when and as he personally judges wise? Or should some sort of control be applied in certain areas? If so, in what cases, and why?

One reason is generally recognized—public danger. This is the basis of restriction in time of war, and often operates by common consent in time of peace. For example, I understand that it is the universal practice of bacteriological laboratories never to supply living pathogens to anyone unless they know him and his work thoroughly.

This recalls the most noteworthy and most successful of all such restrictions imposed by a great profession upon itself from remote antiquity, the Hippocratic oath. From ancient times it has been recognized that the physician holds so much power of life and death in his hands that it is not right and safe to trust it entirely to his individual judgment. The code established more than twenty centuries ago still guides the physician's practice and protects him and his patients alike.

We need a new Hippocratic code today, for the physicist, and for all others who deal with nuclear energy. Someone suggested this last autumn at a meeting of the Conference on Science, Philosophy, and Religion. He went to the heart of the matter. New powers of life and death are in our hands, and we must use them soberly, advisedly, discreetly, and so far as in us lies, in the fear of God.

Investigation of nuclear problems is farther from being foolproof than anything the world had known before. Suppose that by some miracle all danger from the deliberate use of such energy in war or by small malevolent groups could be wholly eliminated. Unless this miracle had completely changed human nature, grave dangers would remain. Some might arise from carelessness or fatigue; some from the desire to "cut corners" and save time or money by relaxing precautions; some from attempts to work on too large a scale, and some, perhaps, from errors in theory, which predicted that a process would be safe when it was not. All of these would be still worse in production than in the laboratory. In both, they combine to make work in this field, for the researcher and the technician alike, a vastly responsible business. It is no place for the negligent, the neurotic, the seeker after personal glory and profit, or the half-baked enthusiast who yearns for a chance to put his individual speculations into practice. It is imperative that other effective controls shall be available before those imposed by military security have been relaxed.

What part we men of science will have in formulating these controls depends upon ourselves. If we show ourselves willing and even eager to establish and enforce, by our own professional means, a sense of responsibility which is commensurate with the situation, we may hope for a truly Hippocratic type of control, in which science has a major place. In these far from millennial years, cooperation with other authorities, international and national, military and civilian, will doubtless be necessary. But if we stand intransigently for the dream of an absolute and irresponsible freedom of the individual scientific worker, we may see some catastrophe which will be followed by a stern Draconian control, in which we have little part.

MEMBERS OF THE CONFERENCE

GUESTS OF PRINCETON UNIVERSITY

J. W. ALEXANDER, Professor in the School of Mathematics, Institute for Advanced Study, Princeton

SAMUEL K. ALLISON, Professor of Physics, University of Chicago

EDOARDO AMALDI, University of Rome, Italy

ERNEST F. BARKER, Professor of Physics, University of Michigan

H. J. BHABHA, Professor of Physics, Tata Institute of Fundamental Research, Bombay, India

P. M. S. BLACKETT, Langworthy Professor of Physics, University of Manchester, England

NIELS BOHR, Professor of Theoretical Physics, University of Copenhagen, Denmark

JOHN H. BOSSHART, Commissioner of Education, New Jersey

GREGORY BREIT, Professor of Physics, University of Wisconsin

P. W. BRIDGMAN, Hollis Professor of Mathematics and Natural Philosophy, Harvard University

C. VERNON CANNON, Clinton Laboratories

S. CHANDRASEKHAR, Professor of Theoretical Astrophysics, Yerkes Observatory, University of Chicago

ARTHUR H. COMPTON, Chancellor, Washington University

KARL T. COMPTON, President, Massachusetts Institute of Technology

JAMES B. CONANT, President, Harvard University

EDWARD U. CONDON, Director, National Bureau of Standards

CHARLES D. CORYELL, Professor of Chemistry, Massachusetts Institute of Technology

PAUL C. CROSS, Professor of Chemistry, Brown University

FARRINGTON DANIELS, Professor of Chemistry, University of Wisconsin

KARL K. DARROW, Bell Telephone Laboratories

C. J. DAVISSON, Bell Telephone Laboratories

G. H. DIEKE, Professor of Physics, Johns Hopkins University

P. A. M. DIRAC, Lucasian Professor of Mathematics, University of Cambridge, England

LEE A. DuBRIDGE, President, California Institute of Technology

FRANK G. DUNNINGTON, Associate Professor of Physics, Rutgers University

W. J. ECKERT, Director of Pure Science, International Business Machines Corp.

E. FERMI, Swift Professor of Physics, University of Chicago

R. P. FEYNMAN, Assistant Professor of Physics, Cornell University

EVERETT J. FORD, Boston English High School, Boston

GAYLORD P. HARNWELL, Professor of Physics, University of Pennsylvania

DAVID HAWKINS, Associate Professor of Philosophy, George Washington University

JOHN C. HOGG, Phillips Exeter Academy, New Hampshire

ALBERT W. HULL, Assistant Director, General Electric Co. Research Laboratories

177

J. C. JACOBSEN, Professor of Physics, University of Copenhagen, Denmark

ZAY JEFFRIES, Vice-President, General Electric Company

FREDERIC JOLIOT, Professor of Physics, Collège de France; High Commissioner of Atomic Energy for France

IRENE CURIE-JOLIOT, Faculté des Sciences, Paris

D. W. KERST, Professor of Physics, University of Illinois

JOHN G. KIRKWOOD, Professor of Chemistry, Cornell University

GEORGE B. KISTIAKOWSKY, Professor of Physical Chemistry, Harvard University

L. KOWARSKI, Collège de France

H. A. KRAMERS, Professor of Theoretical Physics, University of Leyden, Holland

ERNEST O. LAWRENCE, Professor of Physics, University of California

O. MAASS, MacDonald Professor of Physical Chemistry, McGill University, Canada

EDWARD MACK, Professor of Chemistry, Ohio State University

HENRY MARGENAU, Professor of Physics, Yale University

JOSEPH E. MAYER, Professor of Chemistry, University of Chicago

DEAN B. McLAUGHLIN, Professor of Astronomy, University of Michigan

C. E. K. MEES, Vice-President and Director of Research and Development, Eastman Kodak Company

M. G. MESCHERYAKAV, Leningrad Radium Institute, Russia

PHILIP MORRISON, Assistant Professor of Physics, Cornell University

F. S. C. NORTHROP, Professor of Philosophy, Yale University

J. R. OPPENHEIMER, Professor of Theoretical Physics, University of California

M. POLANYI, Professor of Physical Chemistry, University of Manchester, England

I. I. RABI, Professor of Physics, Columbia University

MARCEL SCHEIN, Professor of Physics, University of Chicago

GLENN T. SEABORG, Professor of Chemistry, University of California

HARLOW SHAPLEY, Director, Harvard College Observatory; Paine Professor of Astronomy, Harvard University

MANNE SIEGBAHN, Director, Research Institute for Physics, Royal Academy of Science, Sweden

FRANCIS T. SPAULDING, Commissioner of Education, New York State

C. G. SUITS, Vice-President and Director of Research, General Electric Company

JOHN T. TATE, Professor of Physics, Dean of the College of Science, Literature, and Art, University of Minnesota

WENDELL H. TAYLOR, The Lawrenceville School, New Jersey

CHARLES A. THOMAS, Central Research Director, Monsanto Chemical Company

RICHARD C. TOLMAN, Professor of Physical Chemistry and Mathematical Physics, Dean of the Graduate School, California Institute of Technology

LOUIS A. TURNER, Professor of Physics, University of Iowa

HAROLD C. UREY, Professor of Chemistry, University of Chicago

M. SANDOVAL VALLARTA, Comision Impulsora y Coordinaria de la Investigacion Cientifica, Mexico

J. H. VAN VLECK, Professor of Physics, Harvard University

VICTOR S. VAVILOV, Leningrad University, Russia
OSWALD VEBLEN, Professor in the School of Mathematics, Institute for Advanced Study, Princeton
VICTOR F. WEISSKOPF, Professor of Physics, Massachusetts Institute of Technology
HERMANN WEYL, Professor in the School of Mathematics, Institute for Advanced Study, Princeton
RUPERT WILDT, Associate Professor of Astrophysics, Yale University
E. BRIGHT WILSON, Associate Professor of Chemistry, Harvard University
ROBERT R. WILSON, Associate Professor of Physics, Harvard University
V. K. ZWORYKIN, Associate Director of the Research Laboratories, Radio Corporation of America

MEMBERS OF THE DEPARTMENTS OF ASTRONOMY, CHEMISTRY, PHYSICS, AND MATHEMATICS OF PRINCETON UNIVERSITY WHO ATTENDED THE CONFERENCE

ALYEA, H. N.	LADENBURG, R.	SMYTH, C. P.
ARLEY, N.	LEWIS, L. G.	SMYTH, H. D.
BADIN, E. J.	MONTGOMERY, D. J.	STEWART, J. Q.
BANCROFT, D.	PACSU, E.	TAYLOR, H. S.
BARGMANN, V.	PARLIN, R. B.	TOBOLSKY, A. V.
BLEAKNEY, W.	PEASE, R. N.	TOMLINSON, E. P.
BUSSE, P.	PIERCE, N. L.	TUCKER, A. W.
CHANG, W. Y.	REXFORD, D. R.	TUKEY, J. W.
DICKE, R. II.	REYNOLDS, G. T.	TURKEVICH, J.
DOUGHERTY, G.	ROBERTS, W. VAN B.	VAN VOORHIS, C. C.
EISENHART, L. P.	ROBERTSON, H. P.	WALLIS, E. S.
FULBRIGHT, H. W.	ROGERS, E. M.	WEDDERBURN, J. H. M.
FURMAN, N. H.	RUSSELL, H. N.	WHEELER, J. A.
HAMILTON, D. R.	SCHLEGEL, R.	WHITE, M. G.
HOFSTADTER, R.	SHENSTONE, A. G.	WIGNER, E. P.
KAUZMAN, W. J.	SHERR, R.	WINCKLER, J. R.
KUSAKA, S.	SHIELDS, MARGARET	

INDEX OF NAMES

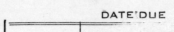
DATE DUE